CALIFORNIA INTEGRATED

P9-DXK-545

elevate science

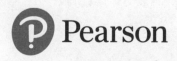

Pearson

Boston, Massachusetts   Chandler, Arizona
Glenview, Illinois   New York, New York

AUTHORS

You're an author!

As you write in this science book, your answers and personal discoveries will be recorded for you to keep, making this book unique to you. That is why you are one of the primary authors of this book.

🖊 **In the space below, print your name, school, town, and state. Then write a short autobiography that includes your interests and accomplishments.**

YOUR NAME ....

SCHOOL ....

TOWN, STATE ....

AUTOBIOGRAPHY ....

....

....

....

....

Your Photo

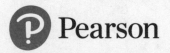

ISBN-13:   978-1-418-31043-1
ISBN-10:   1-418-31043-3
2   19

Program Authors

ZIPPORAH MILLER, Ed.D.

Coordinator for K-12 Science Programs, Anne Arundel County Public Schools

Dr. Zipporah Miller currently serves as the Senior Manager for Organizational Learning with the Anne Arundel County Public School System. Prior to that she served as the K-12 Coordinator for science in Anne Arundel County. She conducts national training to science stakeholders on the Next Generation Science Standards. Dr. Miller also served as the Associate Executive Director for Professional Development Programs and conferences at the National Science Teachers Association (NSTA) and served as a reviewer during the development of Next Generation Science Standards. Dr. Miller holds a doctoral degree from the University of Maryland College Park, a master's degree in school administration and supervision from Bowie State University and a bachelor's degree from Chadron State College.

MICHAEL J. PADILLA, Ph.D.

Professor Emeritus, Eugene P. Moore School of Education, Clemson University, Clemson, South Carolina

Michael J. Padilla taught science in middle and secondary schools, has more than 30 years of experience educating middle-school science teachers, and served as one of the writers of the 1996 U.S. National Science Education Standards. In recent years Mike has focused on teaching science to English Language Learners. His extensive experience as Principal Investigator on numerous National Science Foundation and U.S. Department of Education grants resulted in more than $35 million in funding to improve science education. He served as president of the National Science Teachers Association, the world's largest science teaching organization, in 2005–6.

MICHAEL E. WYSESSION, Ph.D

Professor of Earth and Planetary Sciences, Washington University, St. Louis, Missouri

Author of more than 100 science and science education publications, Dr. Wysession was awarded the prestigious National Science Foundation Presidential Faculty Fellowship and Packard Foundation Fellowship for his research in geophysics, primarily focused on using seismic tomography to determine the forces driving plate tectonics. Dr. Wysession is also a leader in geoscience literacy and education; he is the chair of the Earth Science Literacy Initiative, the author of several popular video lectures on geology in the *Great Courses* series, and a lead writer of the *Next Generation Science Standards**.

REVIEWERS

Program Consultants

Carol Baker
Science Curriculum

Dr. Carol K. Baker is superintendent for Lyons Elementary K-8 School District in Lyons, Illinois. Prior to this, she was Director of Curriculum for Science and Music in Oak Lawn, Illinois. Before this she taught Physics and Earth Science for 18 years. In the recent past, Dr. Baker also wrote assessment questions for ACT (EXPLORE and PLAN), was elected president of the Illinois Science Teachers Association from 2011–2013, and served as a member of the Museum of Science and Industry (Chicago) advisory board. She is a writer of the Next Generation Science Standards. Dr. Baker received her B.S. in Physics and a science teaching certification. She completed her master's of Educational Administration (K-12) and earned her doctorate in Educational Leadership.

Jim Cummins
ELL

Dr. Cummins's research focuses on literacy development in multilingual schools and the role technology plays in learning across the curriculum. *Elevate Science* incorporates research-based principles for integrating language with the teaching of academic content based on Dr. Cummins's work.

Elfrieda Hiebert
Literacy

Dr. Hiebert, a former primary-school teacher, is President and CEO of TextProject, a non-profit aimed at providing open-access resources for instruction of beginning and struggling readers, She is also a research associate at the University of California Santa Cruz. Her research addresses how fluency, vocabulary, and knowledge can be fostered through appropriate texts, and her contributions have been recognized through awards such as the Oscar Causey Award for Outstanding Contributions to Reading Research (Literacy Research Association, 2015), Research to Practice award (American Educational Research Association, 2013), and the William S. Gray Citation of Merit Award for Outstanding Contributions to Reading Research (International Reading Association, 2008).

Content Reviewers

Alex Blom, Ph.D.
Associate Professor
Department Of Physical Sciences
Alverno College
Milwaukee, Wisconsin

Joy Branlund, Ph.D.
Department of Physical Science
Southwestern Illinois College
Granite City, Illinois

Judy Calhoun
Associate Professor
Physical Sciences
Alverno College
Milwaukee, Wisconsin

Stefan Debbert
Associate Professor of Chemistry
Lawrence University
Appleton, Wisconsin

Diane Doser
Professor
Department of Geological Sciences
University of Texas at El Paso
El Paso, Texas

Rick Duhrkopf, Ph.D.
Department of Biology
Baylor University
Waco, Texas

Jennifer Liang
University of Minnesota Duluth
Duluth, Minnesota

Heather Mernitz, Ph.D.
Associate Professor of Physical Sciences
Alverno College
Milwaukee, Wisconsin

Joseph McCullough, Ph.D.
Cabrillo College
Aptos, California

Katie M. Nemeth, Ph.D.
Assistant Professor
College of Science and Engineering
University of Minnesota Duluth
Duluth, Minnesota

Maik Pertermann
Department of Geology
Western Wyoming Community College
Rock Springs, Wyoming

Scott Rochette
Department of the Earth Sciences
The College at Brockport
  State University of New York
Brockport, New York

David Schuster
Washington University in St Louis
St. Louis, Missouri

Shannon Stevenson
Department of Biology
University of Minnesota Duluth
Duluth, Minnesota

Paul Stoddard, Ph.D.
Department of Geology and
  Environmental Geosciences
Northern Illinois University
DeKalb, Illinois

Nancy Taylor
American Public University
Charles Town, West Virginia

Teacher Reviewers

Rita Armstrong
Los Cerritos Middle School
Thousand Oaks, California

Tyler C. Britt, Ed.S.
Curriculum & Instructional
Practice Coordinator
Raytown Quality Schools
Raytown, Missouri

Holly Bowser
Barstow High School
Barstow, California

David Budai
Coachella Valley Unified School District
Coachella, California

A. Colleen Campos
Grandview High School
Aurora, Colorado

Jodi DeRoos
Mojave River Academy
Colton, California

Colleen Duncan
Moore Middle School
Redlands, California

Nicole Hawke
Westside Elementary
Thermal, California

Margaret Henry
Lebanon Junior High School
Lebanon, Ohio

Ashley Humphrey
Riverside Preparatory Elementary
Oro Grande, California

Adrianne Kilzer
Riverside Preparatory Elementary
Oro Grande, California

Danielle King
Barstow Unified School District
Barstow, California

Kathryn Kooyman
Riverside Preparatory Elementary
Oro Grande, California

Esther Leonard M.Ed. and L.M.T.
Gifted and Talented Implementation Specialist
San Antonio Independent School District
San Antonio, Texas

Diana M. Maiorca, M.Ed.
Los Cerritos Middle School
Thousand Oaks, California

Kevin J. Maser, Ed.D.
H. Frank Carey Jr/Sr High School
Franklin Square, New York

Corey Mayle
Brogden Middle School
Durham, North Carolina

Keith McCarthy
George Washington Middle School
Wayne, New Jersey

Rudolph Patterson
Cobalt Institute of Math and Science
Victorville, California

Yolanda O. Peña
John F. Kennedy Junior High School
West Valley City, Utah

Stacey Phelps
Mojave River Academy
Oro Grande, California

Susan Pierce
Bryn Mawr Elementary
Redlands Unified School District
Redlands, California

Cristina Ramos
Mentone Elementary School
Redlands Unified School District
Mentone, California

Mary Regis
Franklin Elementary School
Redlands, California

Bryna Selig
Gaithersburg Middle School
Gaithersburg, Maryland

Pat (Patricia) Shane, Ph.D.
STEM & ELA Education Consultant
Chapel Hill, North Carolina

Elena Valencia
Coral Mountain Academy
Coachella, California

Janelle Vecchio
Mission Elementary School
Redlands, California

Brittney Wells
Riverside Preparatory Elementary
Oro Grande, California

Kristina Williams
Sequoia Middle School
Newbury Park, California

Safety Reviewers

Douglas Mandt, M.S.
Science Education Consultant
Edgewood, Washington

Juliana Textley, Ph.D.
Author, NSTA books on school science safety
Adjunct Professor
Lesley University
Cambridge, Massachusetts

HANDS-ON LABS
иConnect
иInvestigate
иDemonstrate

HANDS-ON LABS

и**Connect**
и**Investigate**
и**Demonstrate**

HANDS-ON LABS

uConnect
uInvestigate
uDemonstrate

Elevate your thinking!

California Elevate Science takes science to a whole new level and lets you take ownership of your learning. Explore science in the world around you. Investigate how things work. Think critically and solve problems! *California Elevate Science* helps you think like a scientist, so you're ready for a world of discoveries.

Exploring California

California spotlights explore California phenomena. Topic Quests help connect lesson concepts together and reflect 3-dimensional learning.

- Science concepts organized around phenomena
- Topics weave together 3-D learning
- Engineering focused on solving problems and improving designs

California Spotlight
Instructional Segment 2

Before the Topics
Identify the Problem

California Flood Management

Phenomenon In February of 2017, workers at the Oroville Dam were forced to use the

Student Discourse

California Elevate Science promotes active discussion, higher order thinking and analysis and prepares you for high school through:

- High-level write-in prompts
- Evidence-based arguments
- Practice in speaking and writing

Model It

Crystalline and Amorphous Solids
Figure 5 ✏ A pat of butter is an amorphous solid. The particles that make up the butter are not arranged in a regular pattern. The sapphire gem stones are crystalline solids. Draw what you think the particles look like in a crystalline solid.

☑ **READING CHECK** **Explain** In your own words, explain the main differences between crystalline solids and amorphous solids.

_____

_____

_____

_____

Quest CHECK-IN

In this lesson, you learned what happens to the particles of substances during melting, freezing, evaporation, boiling, condensation, and sublimation. You also thought about how thermal energy plays a role in these changes of state.

Predict Why do you need to take the temperature of the surroundings into consideration when designing a system with materials that can change state?

Academic Vocabulary

In orange juice, bits of pulp are suspended in liquid. Explain what you think *suspended* means.

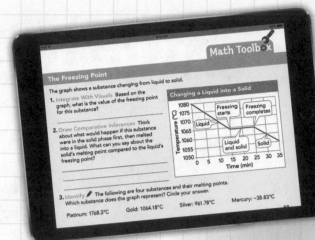

Build Literacy Skills

By connecting science to other disciplines like:

- Mathematics
- Reading and Writing
- STEM/Engineering

Focus on Inquiry

Case studies put you in the shoes of a scientist to solve real-world mysteries using real data. You will be able to:

- Analyze data
- Formulate claims
- Build evidence-based arguments

Enter the Digital Classroom

Virtual labs, 3-D expeditions, and dynamic videos take science beyond the classroom.

- Open-ended virtual labs
- Google Expeditions and field trips
- NBC Learn videos

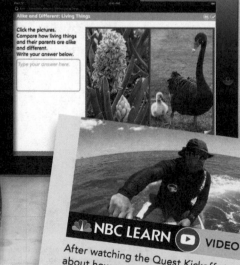

Go to PearsonRealize.com to access your digital course.

Elevate Science combines the best science narrative with a robust online program. Throughout the lessons, digital support is presented at point of use to enhance your learning experience.

Online Resources

Pearson Realize™ is your online science class. This digital-learning environment includes:

- Student eTEXT
- Instructor eTEXT
- Project-Based Learning
- Virtual Labs
- Interactivities
- Videos
- Assessments
- Study Tools
- and more!

Digital Features

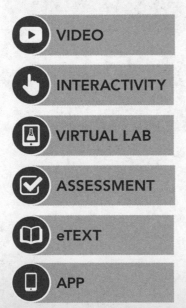

- VIDEO
- INTERACTIVITY
- VIRTUAL LAB
- ASSESSMENT
- eTEXT
- APP

Keep an eye out for these **icons**, which indicate the different ways your textbook is enhanced online.

Digital activities are located throughout the narrative to deepen your understanding of scientific concepts.

INTERACTIVITY

Interpret models of relationships in various ecosystems.

Spotlight on the Anchoring Phenomenon

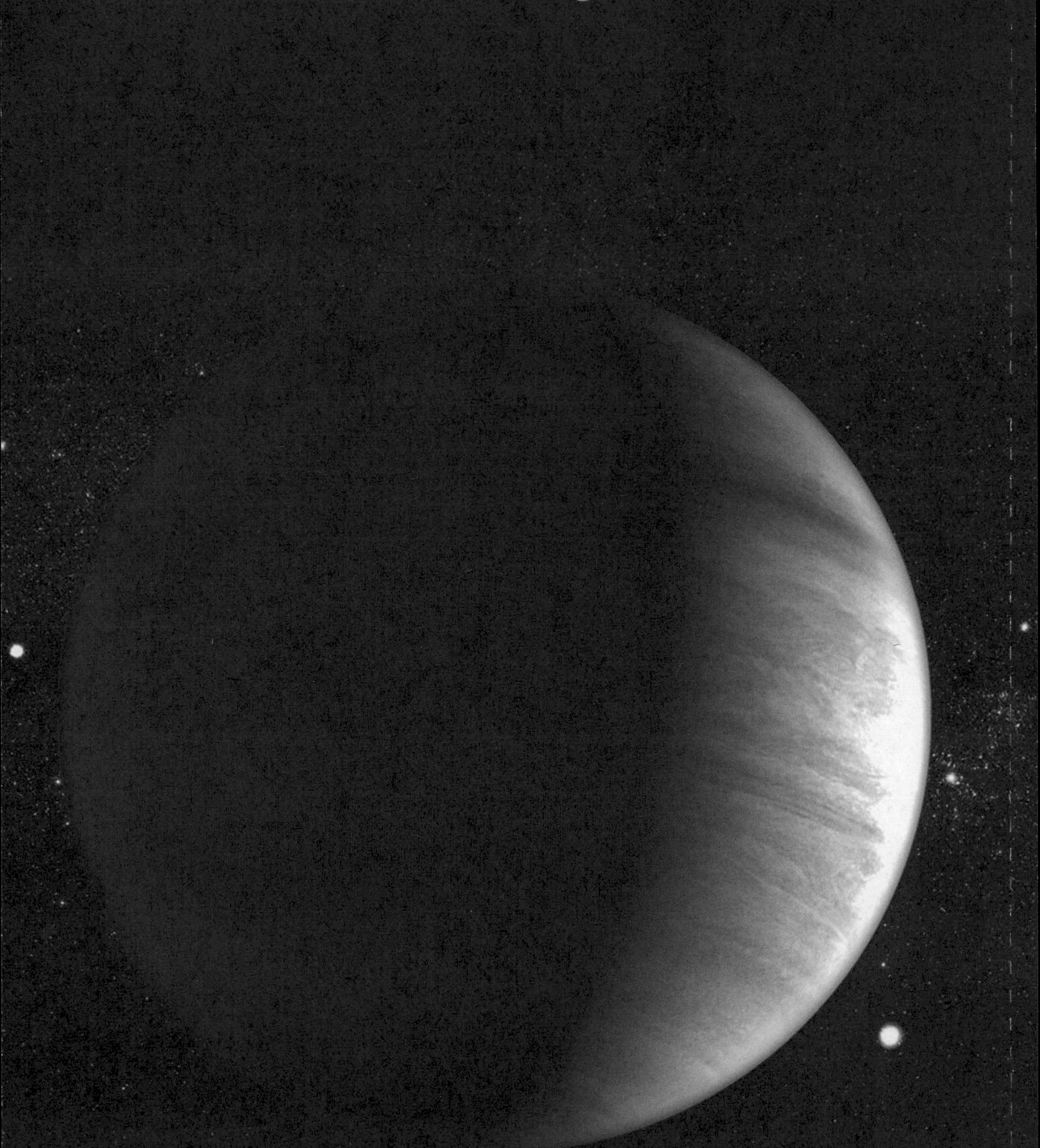

How do noncontact forces affect the movement of objects in space?

Explore It

Look at the picture. What do you observe? What questions do you have about the phenomenon? Write your observations and questions in the space below.

....

....

....

....

....

....

....

....

....

....

....

....

....

....

....

....

....

....

....

....

MS-ESS1-1, MS-ESS1-2, MS-ESS1-3, MS-PS2-3, MS-PS2-5

Inquiry

- How can an object influence the motion of another object without touching it?
- Does Earth's force of gravity attract other objects equally?

Topics

An artist's interpretation of 51 Pegasi-b

Before the Topics
Identify the Problem

California's Planet Hunters

Phenomenon In 1995, a team of Swiss astronomers announced that they had discovered a planet orbiting 51 Pegasi, a star about 50 light years away from Earth. They named the planet 51 Pegasi-b. Within a few days, a team at Lick Observatory near San Jose, California, confirmed the discovery using its powerful telescopes. Since then, thousands more extrasolar planets, or exoplanets, have been discovered. Researchers in California have helped find many of them.

Lick Observatory, Hamilton, California

Sitting atop Mount Hamilton in California's Diablo Range is an observatory that has been used for space exploration since 1888. Several of Jupiter's moons were discovered from there, and it was the first facility to accurately measure the distance from Earth to the moon using a laser.

In recent years, many researchers at Lick have turned their attention to the search for exoplanets. Finding exoplanets is not easy because they are so very far away. Even the strongest telescopes cannot see planets revolving around distant stars. But researchers at Lick have figured out how to look for evidence of planets by observing the movement of stars. As planets and other objects orbit a star, their gravitational pull causes the star to move slightly, or wobble. When researchers detect a wobble using this method (the radial velocity method), they know something is orbiting the star.

Lick's Automated Planet Finder (APF) is the world's first robotic telescope that can detect planets outside our solar system. Because it does not require a human operator, the telescope is able to hunt for exoplanets any night when conditions are clear enough.

The Automated Planet Finder (APF) at Lick Observatory

SEP Construct Explanations
In your own words, describe the method that is used at the Lick Observatory to identify planets.

....

....

....

....

....

....

....

....

....

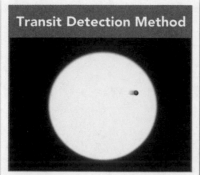

Transit Detection Method

As this exoplanet transits its star, it blocks out a tiny portion of the star's light. Sensitive instruments on *Kepler* can detect these slight changes in brightness.

By the end of 2017, five years beyond its planned lifetime, the *Kepler* mission had detected 4,496 candidate planets orbiting stars in 2,650 solar systems. Of those candidates, 3,558 were confirmed exoplanets.

Ames Research Center, Mountain View, California

Not far from Lick Observatory, in the area known as Silicon Valley, you can find NASA's Ames Research Center. This facility opened in 1939 and has since been involved in hundreds of space missions.

Ames is deeply involved in the search for exoplanets and manages the *Kepler* mission. NASA launched the *Kepler* space observatory in March 2009. Outfitted with a powerful telescope that could search the Milky Way for evidence of exoplanets, *Kepler* used a method called transit detection to look for objects moving in front of distant stars. Like a fly on a movie projector, even a small planet will cause the star's light to dim.

Like many spacecraft, *Kepler* relied on energy from the sun to make its own electricity and carry out its functions. An array of solar panels attached to the craft faced toward the sun at all times. Every three months in its orbit around the sun, the spacecraft rolled 90 degrees to keep its panels facing the sun.

Designed to last 3.5 years, *Kepler* ran into difficulty by 2013. Rather than end the mission, engineers made some modifications to extend its run time. Known as *K2*, the new mission continued to collect data about exoplanets.

Planet Type	Candidate Exoplanets	Confirmed Exoplanets
Neptune-like	1,765	1,414
Super-Earth	1,297	52
Terrestrial	916	881
Gas Giant	455	1,186
Unknown	63	25
Total	4,496	3,558

SEP Analyze Data Multiple observations are needed to validate the discovery of confirmed exoplanets. Based on the data in the table, what is the probability that a *Kepler* candidate exoplanet could eventually be confirmed by multiple observations?

....

....

....

Jet Propulsion Laboratory, Pasadena, California

Engineers at NASA's Jet Propulsion Laboratory (JPL) in Pasadena, California, have been designing and building spacecraft since 1958, when they built the first U.S. satellite launched into space. Since then, JPL engineers have been involved in major space exploration missions.

Since 2003, JPL has been overseeing a mission to help astronomers find exoplanets. The mission uses the *Spitzer* Space Telescope, which was built to detect infrared light. By examining infrared light from distant stars, the telescope is able to hunt for exoplanets. *Spitzer* uses a method called gravitational microlensing that relies on an unusual phenomenon.

When one star passes in front of another star, the light from the blocked star actually bends around the blocking star because of the gravitational force of the closer star. The effect is that the infrared light from the blocked star is focused and gets brighter. If a planet is orbiting the blocking star and it lines up in the right way, then it can also cause the blocked star to shine brighter. The timing has to be perfect to be successful, and they don't get many chances to get it right. But the major advantage of this method over the others is that it can be used to observe stars that are much farther away.

The *Spitzer* Telescope observes infrared light from distant stars to identify exoplanets.

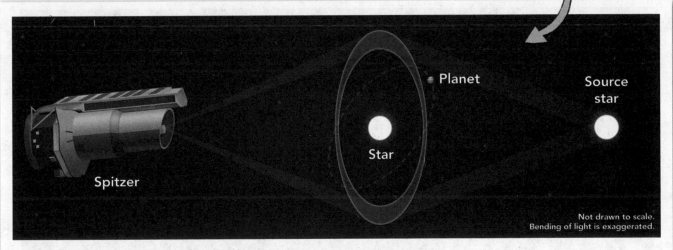

Planet

Source star

Star

Spitzer

Not drawn to scale.
Bending of light is exaggerated.

Analyze Costs and Benefits What is the major advantage and disadvantage of the *Spitzer* Space Telescope?

....

....

....

....

Potentially Habitable Planets

Astronomers have discovered thousands of planets outside our solar system since the first one was discovered in 1995. They are most excited about the ones that they consider potentially habitable. But what makes an exoplanet potentially habitable? Astronomers think the best candidates for supporting life are those that are most similar to Earth.

An important part of finding a planet that is like Earth is finding one that is in what astronomers call the habitable zone. This is the area that is neither too close nor too far away from the star it orbits. This keeps the planet at the right temperature: not too hot and not too cold.

Being at a "just-right" temperature is important for a planet to support life because it allows for liquid water to exist. The habitable zone is different for different star systems. The habitable zone in a system with a cooler star may be much closer to the star. The habitable zone in a system with a hotter star would be farther away.

Astronomers also think that habitable planets would be rocky like Earth, not gaseous like Jupiter or Saturn. They look for planets that are close in size to Earth. They believe that planets that are about the same size as Earth will have a rocky surface, while those that are much bigger will likely be gas giants.

The habitable zone is also known as the Goldilocks Zone.

Too hot

Just right

Too cold

Habitable zone

CCC Cause and Effect 🖊 Suppose the star in the diagram were cooler and dimmer. Draw lines on the diagram to indicate where the habitable zone would be.

Planetary Magnetic Fields

Astronomers also look for evidence of magnetic fields when trying to determine whether or not a planet is capable of supporting life. Scientists have recently learned that part of what makes Earth ideal for life is the magnetic field surrounding it. The magnetic field protects our planet from solar radiation and the solar winds that would otherwise destroy our atmosphere and harm living things.

In exploring our own solar system, spacecraft outfitted with magnetometers can detect whether a planet has a magnetic field. Astronomers have determined, for example, that Earth, Mercury, and the gas giants have magnetic fields, while Venus and Mars do not. But because exoplanets are so far away, there are currently no reliable ways to determine whether one has a magnetic field. Researchers and engineers are working hard to develop some possible strategies and solutions. Perhaps in the near future, they will find one that works.

Earth's magnetic field protects it from solar winds.

SEP Communicate Information Why do astronomers hypothesize that exoplanets that are most like Earth might be planets capable of supporting life?

....

....

....

....

Electricity and Magnetism

Investigative Phenomenon
How can you develop and use models to explain the factors that affect the strength of electric and magnetic forces?

What generates the electricity to power this space telescope?

MS-PS2-3 Ask questions about data to determine the factors that affect the strength of electric and magnetic forces.

MS-PS2-5 Conduct an investigation and evaluate the experimental design to provide evidence that fields exist between objects exerting forces on each other even though the objects are not in contact.

MS-PS3-2 Develop a model to describe that when the arrangement of objects interacting at a distance changes, different amounts of potential energy are stored in the system.

EP&CIa Students should be developing an understanding that the goods produced by natural systems are essential to human life and to the functioning of our economies and cultures.

EP&CIIb Students should be developing an understanding that methods used to extract, harvest, transport, and consume natural resources influence the geographic extent, composition, biological diversity, and viability of natural systems.

HANDS-ON LAB

uConnect Make observations to determine the north and south poles of a magnet.

What questions do you have about the phenomenon?

....

....

....

....

....

....

....

....

....

....

Quest PBL

How can you lift an object without making contact?

STEM **Figure It Out** In Japan, South Korea, and China, you can hop on a train that uses electromagnets to levitate above a rail and travel at very high speeds. The technology is the result of years of research and testing by electrical and mechanical engineers. In this STEM Quest, you will explore how you can use electromagnetism to lift or raise objects without coming into contact with them. In digital activities, you will investigate electric and magnetic forces. By applying what you have learned, you will perform technical tasks as you design, build, and test a device that can levitate objects.

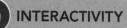 **INTERACTIVITY**

Light as a Feather?

MS-PS2-3, MS-PS2-5, MS-PS3-2
(Also EP&CIa, EP&CIIb)

NBC LEARN ▶ VIDEO

After watching the video, which examines some industrial applications of magnets and electromagnets, list two examples of objects that you use every day that rely on magnets or electromagnets.

Example 1

....

....

....

....

Example 2

....

....

....

....

Quest CHECK-IN

IN LESSON 1

STEM What kinds of forces are exerted by positive and negative charges? Think about how charged objects interact, and apply what you have learned to your levitating device.

👆 **INTERACTIVITY**

Apply Electrical Forces

Quest CHECK-IN

IN LESSON 2

STEM How can you use magnets to build a levitation device? Develop possible design solutions by exploring magnetic forces.

HANDS-ON LAB

Tracking Levitation

Quest CHECK-IN

IN LESSON 3

STEM How can you control the strength of your device? Build an electromagnet and explore how you can incorporate the technology into your device.

HANDS-ON LAB

Building an Electromagnet

Magnetism is used to elevate this "maglev" train several centimeters above the tracks and also to propel it forward. The absence of friction between the train and the track allows the maglev train to achieve speeds as great as 600 kilometers per hour! Maglev trains move efficiently, which may help to reduce both consumption of fossil fuels and air pollution. A similar system has been under consideration to connect the cities of Anaheim, California and Las Vegas, Nevada.

Quest CHECK-IN

IN LESSON 4

STEM How can you refine your levitating device to improve your results? Redesign and retest your device using electromagnets.

HANDS-ON LAB

Electrifying Levitation

Quest FINDINGS

Complete the Quest!

Apply what you've learned by describing other scenarios in your daily life in which electromagnets could be used to make a task easier.

👆 **INTERACTIVITY**

Reflect on Your Levitating Device

LESSON

1 Electric Force

HANDS-ON LAB

uInvestigate Use a device to detect electric charges.

MS-PS2-5 Conduct an investigation and evaluate the experimental design to provide evidence that fields exist between objects exerting forces on each other even though the objects are not in contact.

MS-PS3-2 Develop a model to describe that when the arrangement of objects interacting at a distance changes, different amounts of potential energy are stored in the system.

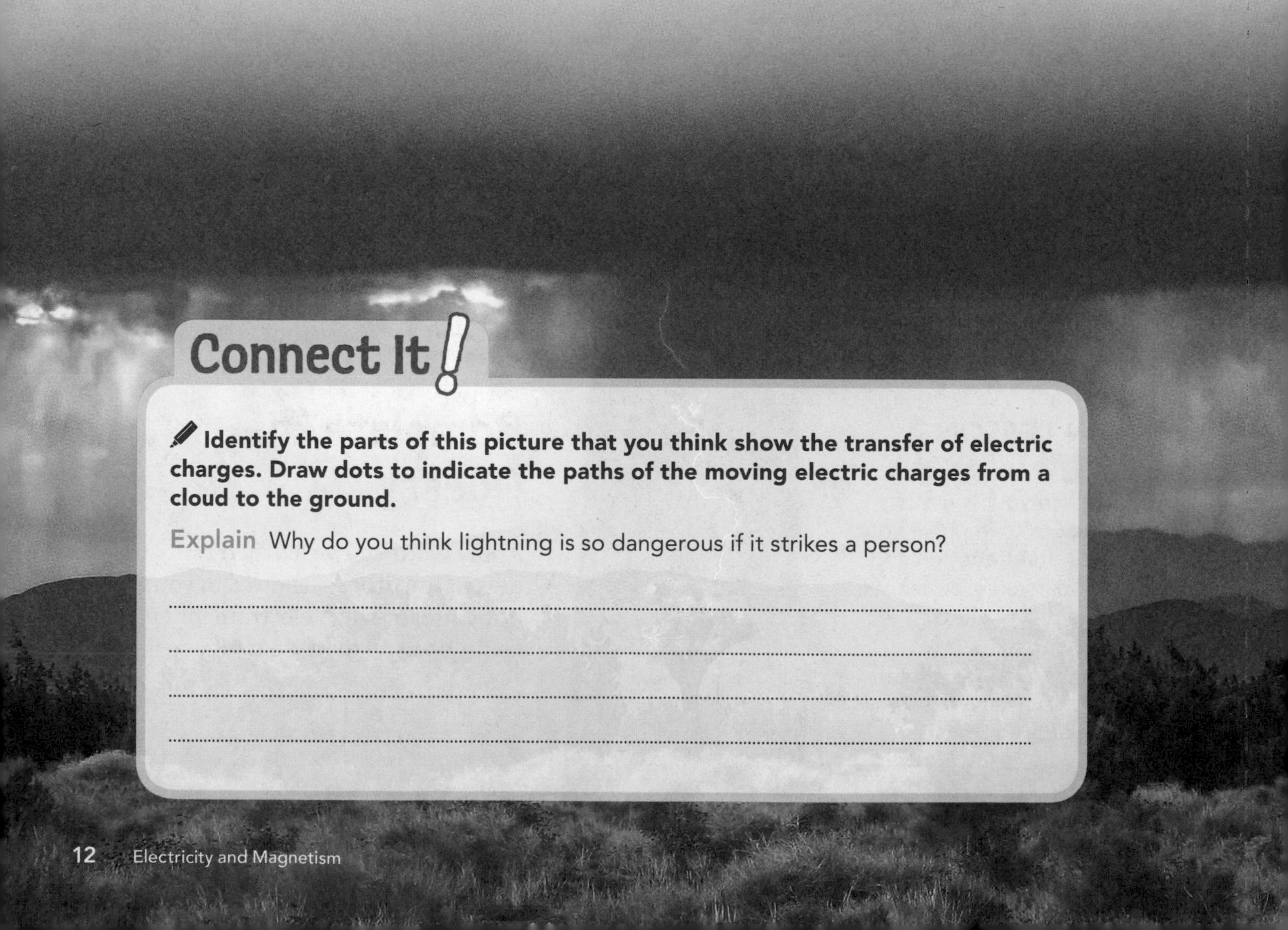

Connect It!

Identify the parts of this picture that you think show the transfer of electric charges. Draw dots to indicate the paths of the moving electric charges from a cloud to the ground.

Explain Why do you think lightning is so dangerous if it strikes a person?

....

....

....

....

Electric Force, Fields, and Energy

Did you know that there are electric charges, forces, and fields inside your body? You might not see them or feel them, but they are everywhere!

Electric force is an interaction that occurs between two or more charged particles. Some particles have a positive charge and some have a negative charge. A particle with no charge is neutral. If an object has more positive than negative particles, then the object has a positive charge. If an object has more negative than positive particles, then the object has a negative charge. If an object has an equal number of positive and negative particles, then the particles cancel each other out and the object has no charge.

Charged particles can move in and out of an object. If a positively charged object gains negatively charged particles, the object becomes negatively charged. If a negatively charged object loses negatively charged particles, so that there are more positively charged particles, then the object becomes positively charged.

If you have ever watched a lightning storm, as in **Figure 1**, you have seen a dramatic display of electric charges. The lightning bolts are made up of moving charged particles.

☑ **CHECK POINT** **Summarize Text** How can a neutral object become negatively charged?

....

....

Lightning Storm

Figure 1 Lightning bolts like these photographed in the Mojave Desert near Hesperia, California, can travel from clouds to the ground. They can also travel within a cloud and between clouds. These streaks of light are the result of the movement of electric charges.

Electric Field Lines

Figure 2 Images A and B show the field lines around single charges. Image C shows the field lines around a positive charge and a negative charge next to each other. Where field lines are closer together, the electric field is stronger.

1. SEP Use Models Is the electric field stronger within the white rectangle or within the blue rectangle in image C?

....

2. Draw Conclusions Is the electric field stronger close to the charges or farther away from the charges?

....

☑ CHECK POINT **Integrate with Visuals** In which direction would a positive charge move if it were placed in between the positive and negative charges in image C?

....

....

Electric Force The force between charged particles or objects is called **electric force**. If a positively charged particle and negatively charged particle come close together, an attraction draws them together. On the other hand, if two negatively charged particles come close together, they repel each other because they both are negatively charged. The electric force causes them to move apart. In simplest terms, opposite charges attract, and like charges repel. When it moves a charge, the electric force transfers kinetic energy to the charge.

The strength of the electric force depends on the distance between the charges. For example, when a positively charged particle or object is close to another positively charged particle, a strong force between them pushes them away from each other. As they move apart, the force between them becomes weaker. The strength of the electric force also depends on the amount of charge present. When more charge is involved, the electric force is stronger. For instance, three positively charged particles attract a negatively charged particle more strongly than one positvely charged particle alone.

Electric Fields Two charged particles will experience electric forces between them without even touching. How is this possible? An electric charge has an invisible **electric field** around it—a region around the charged particle or object where the electric force is exerted on other charged particles or objects. Electric fields can be represented with field lines, as in **Figure 2**. They point in the direction that the force would push a positive charge, which is called a *test object*. Field lines around a positively charged object point away from the object. They indicate that the object would repel a positive charge. Field lines around a negatively charged object point toward the object. The negatively charged object would attract a positive charge. When multiple charges are in the same area, the field lines show a more complicated combination of the two fields.

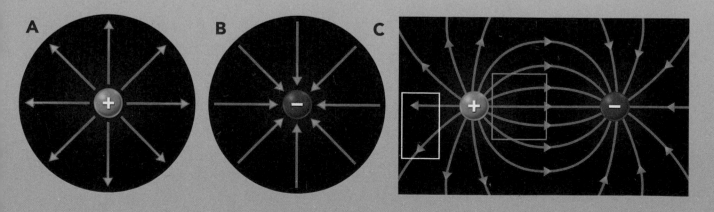

Charges and Potential Energy When forces are in action, you can be sure that energy is also involved. Suppose you have a system that consists of two opposite charges and their interaction. If you pull the opposite charges away from each other, the potential energy of the system increases. You can understand this by comparing it to gravitational potential energy. Gravity is an attractive force. When you lift an object higher above Earth, you apply a force and transfer energy to it. The gravitational potential energy increases. When you drop the object, the force of gravity pulls the object to the ground and the gravitational potential energy decreases. The force between opposite charges is also an attractive force. As you apply a force to move opposite charges away from each other, the electrical potential energy of the system increases. When the electric force between opposite charges pulls them together naturally, the potential energy of the system decreases, as shown in **Figure 3**.

Potential energy changes in a different way for two like charges. Two like charges naturally repel each other. An outside force is not needed to move them apart. Therefore, as the electric force between two like charges pushes them away from each other, the potential energy of the system decreases.

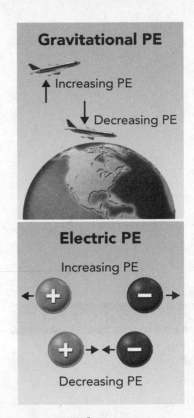

Potential Energy
Figure 3 Electric potential energy behaves much like gravitational potential energy.

Question It !

Students are conducting an experiment to provide evidence that electric fields exert forces on objects even when the objects are not in contact. They use pith balls hanging from strings. These pith balls have been charged by touching another charged object. The students drew this diagram to show the result of their experiment. Pith balls are small balls that pick up charge easily, but any sort of lightweight balls would show the same effect.

1. CCC Cause and Effect When the two pith balls have opposite charges, they are naturally pulled together due to the attractive electric force between them. If you pull the two pith balls away from each other, what happens to the potential energy of the system? Explain.

....

....

....

2. Cite Textual Evidence How do the details of this experiment provide evidence that electric fields exert forces on the pith balls, even when they are not in contact?

....

Electric Current and Circuits

Electric charges play a major role in daily life. Any time you use electricity, you are using energy from electric charges that are in motion. The charges flow through materials as water flows down a stream. The continuous flow of charge is known as **electric current**. Current is measured as a rate in units called *amperes*. The abbreviation for this unit is A. The number of amperes describes the amount of charge that passes by a given point each second.

Current flows through paths known as *circuits*. A circuit is a path that runs in a loop. A basic electric circuit contains a source of energy connected with wires to a device that runs on electricity. Current flows from the source of energy, through the wires, through the electric device, and back to the source.

Voltage Why do charges flow through a circuit? They move because of differences in potential energy. Current flows from a point of higher potential energy to a point of lower potential energy in the circuit. For instance, a battery, like the one shown in **Figure 4**, has one end where current has a higher potential energy per charge than it has at the other end of the battery. This difference in electrical potential energy per charge is called *voltage*. The voltage acts like a force that causes current to flow. Voltage is measured in units of volts. The abbreviation for this unit is V.

Literacy Connection

Integrate with Visuals
🖉 Draw dots and arrows to represent current flowing through the circuit.

Current in Circuits

Figure 4 The following circuit shows a battery connected to a light bulb.

1. Based on potential energy, which direction should the current flow? Explain your answer.

....

....

....

....

....

....

....

2. In the process that moves current through the system shown, what form of energy is the input? The output?

....

....

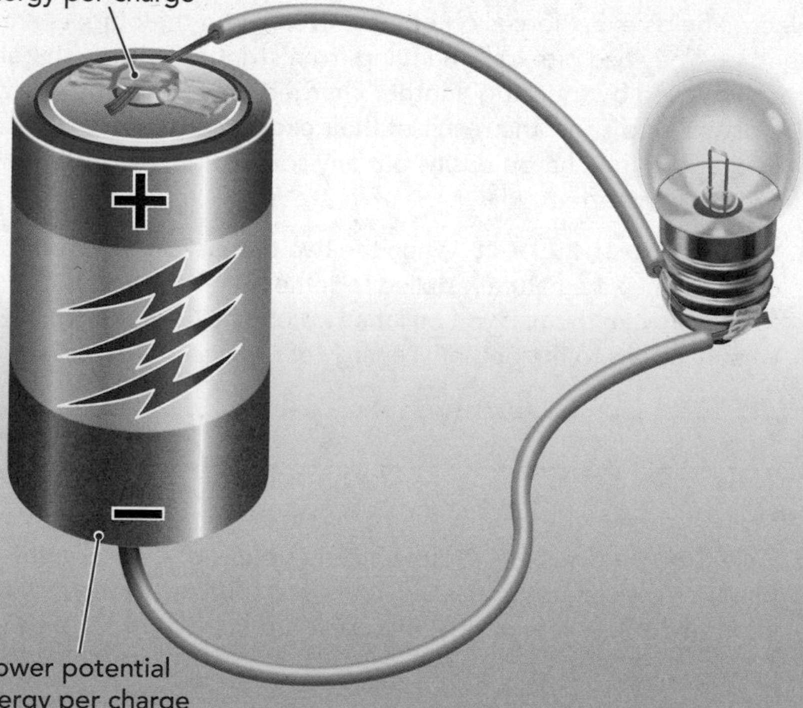

higher potential energy per charge

lower potential energy per charge

Energy in Circuits
You can compare a charge in a circuit to an object in the gravitational field of Earth. When an object falls, the force of gravity pulls the object from a position of higher potential energy to a position of lower potential energy. You give that potential energy back when you lift the object up to its initial position. A battery gives energy back to charges as well. Inside the battery, the energy from chemical reactions is converted to electrical energy, which increases the potential energy of the system of electric charges. Charges leave the battery through the high-potential terminal, move through the circuit, and return to the low-potential terminal.

Current and Resistance
What are the charges that flow through a circuit? They are negatively charged particles. Historically, the current is described as flowing in the direction in which positive charges would move. However, these particles are actually negatively charged. So the direction of current is opposite to the direction of the flow of negatively charged particles.

Some materials have negatively charged particles that are tightly bound and difficult to move. Those materials, called insulators, do not allow charge to flow. Therefore, they have a high resistance to electric current. On the other hand, some materials have negatively charged particles that are more loosely bound and easier to move. Those materials are **conductors**—they allow charge to flow more freely (**Figure 5**). Just as there are insulators and conductors of heat, there are insulators and conductors of charge. Insulators of charge are materials such as rubber, wood, and glass, while conductors include materials such as silver, copper, and gold.

☑ CHECK POINT **Explain** Describe why current flows through a circuit, and explain why some materials allow charges to flow more easily than others.

....

....

....

....

Conductors and Insulators of Charge
Figure 5 Electrical conductors and insulators are all around you. Label each of these common items as a conductor or an insulator.

SEP Construct Explanations
Which of the materials used to make these objects would you use in a circuit? Explain why.

....

....

....

....

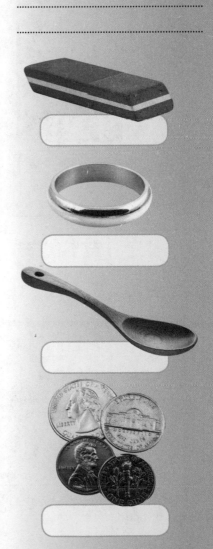

Charging by Induction

Figure 6 If your finger has a buildup of charge, it may induce a charge in a doorknob. Negatively charged particles in the doorknob move away from your finger to the opposite side of the doorknob.

Static Electricity

Most objects are made of equal amounts of negatively and positively charged particles. As a result, these objects are neutral. Charge cannot be created or destroyed, but it can be transferred. The transfer of charge happens by moving negatively charged particles from one object to another or from one part of an object to another. Those charges do not flow like current. Instead, they remain static, meaning they stay in place. This buildup of charge on an object is called **static electricity**.

Methods of Charging
Objects can become charged by four methods: conduction, friction, induction, and polarization. Charging by conduction is simply the movement of charge by direct contact between objects. The object that is more negatively charged transfers negatively charged particles to the other object. Charging by friction occurs when two objects rub against each other and negatively charged particles move from one object to the other. You can see the effect if you stick two pieces of tape together and then pull them apart. Objects become charged by induction without even touching. The electric field of one charged object repels the negatively charged particles of the other object. So the second object ends up with a buildup of charge on its opposite side, as in **Figure 6**. Polarization is similar except the negatively charged particles only move to the opposite side of their atoms rather than to the opposite side of the entire object. See if you can identify the methods of charging in **Figure 7**.

Interactions with Static Electricity
Figure 7 Label the method of charging in each image as conduction, friction, induction, or polarization.

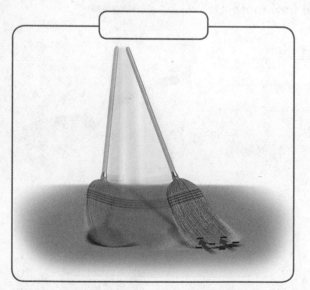

The broom becomes charged as it sweeps across the floor.

Bits of paper are attracted to the broom's negative charge. In the paper, negatively charged particles of the atoms move to the opposite side of each atom, away from the broom.

Balloon and Paper

Figure 8 ✏ **CCC Energy and Matter** The balloon attracts the paper because of static electricity. Draw the charges on the balloon and on the bits of paper. Then, describe what happens to potential energy as you pull the bits of paper off of the balloon.

....
....
....
....
....

▶ **VIDEO**

Watch and learn how lightning works.

👆 **INTERACTIVITY**

Develop a model to show the potential energy of a system involving electric forces.

Potential Energy and Static Electricity If you rub a balloon, you might be surprised that it can pick up bits of paper. The balloon attracts the paper because of static electricity. Rubbing the balloon causes negatively charged particles to transfer to it. The charged balloon polarizes the bits of paper. Because the surface of the balloon is negatively charged and the surface of the paper is positively charged, they attract each other, as in **Figure 8**. As the bits of paper move toward the balloon, the potential energy of the system decreases. When you pull the bits of paper off of the balloon, you apply a force to them. The potential energy of the system of objects increases as you move the paper away from the balloon.

Static Discharge Most objects that become charged eventually lose their charge to the air. Charge transfers to or from the air until the charged object is neutral. The process of discharging can sometimes cause a spark or shock when the negatively charged particles transfer. If you have ever reached to pet a cat and experienced a shock, it was the result of static discharge.

Lightning is also the result of static discharge. Water droplets in the clouds become charged due to their motion through the air during a storm. Negatively charged particles then move from areas of negative charge to areas of positive charge. The movement of charge produces the intense spark that you see as a lightning bolt.

📓 **Reflect** Describe a time when you experienced a shock from static electricity. Explain what happened in terms of electric charges.

☑ **CHECK POINT** **Describe** What happens to charges during static discharge?

....

19

MS-PS2-5, MS-PS3-2

1. Describe Why are conductors better than insulators to carry electric current?

....

....

....

2. Predict Phenomena A positively charged particle is placed next to an negatively charged object. In which direction does the positively charged particle move? Explain why.

....

....

....

....

....

3. CCC Cause and Effect If you move two objects with opposite charges apart, what happens to their potential energy? Explain your response.

....

....

....

....

....

4. SEP Develop Models ✏ After Sandra combs her hair, she notices that her hair moves toward the comb. Draw a model of the comb and Sandra's hair. Show the charges on both the comb and the hair. Describe what occurred to charge the comb and then to charge the hair.

....

....

....

....

....

....

Quest CHECK-IN

In this lesson, you learned about the interactions of electric charges through forces and fields. You also discovered how potential energy plays a role in the flow of current. Additionally, you explored how charges behave in static electricity.

SEP Design Solutions How might electric fields become involved in your levitation device?

....

....

....

👆 INTERACTIVITY

Apply Electrical Forces

Go online to explore how the interaction between charged particles could be used to develop a design for a levitation device.

Thunder and Lightning, An
African Folktale

Many, many years ago, Thunder and Lightning lived on Earth in a village alongside humans. Thunder was a mother sheep. Her son, Lightning, was a ram.

Thunder and Lightning, however, were not held in high regard by the villagers. Lightning had a terrible temper. Whenever he felt offended by someone's words or actions, he exploded in a fiery rage, burning everything to the ground in his path. Plant, trees, animals, and even villager's homes were often destroyed.

Seeing her child act so badly, Thunder would erupt in anger. She raised her voice, booming and shouting at him in the hopes he would stop.

The villagers were greatly distressed by the fires started by Lightning and the ensuing racket caused by Thunder. As they often did, they went to the village elder to complain.

The village elder tried everything in his power to keep the peace. But no matter how many times he begged and pleaded with Thunder and Lightning, the two would be back to their old ways in no time.

One day, the village elder called together all the villagers to discuss the problem. Everyone agreed that the only solution was to keep the pair as far away as possible from the village.

So the village elder thought it over, and he banished Thunder and Lightning from Earth to live in the sky. The villagers were relieved, thinking their village would finally be peaceful.

But, as is often the case, things did work out as expected. Occasionally, Lightning still gets angry and sends some fire down to Earth. And, a moment later, you can hear his mother get angry with him.

CONNECT TO YOU

Many myths and folktales from around the world attempt to explain events and phenomena in the natural world. In your science notebook, write your own myth or folktale to explain something in nature.

② Magnetic Force

HANDS-ON LAB

uInvestigate Discover how you can use a magnet to tell the difference between real and fake coins.

MS-PS2-5 Conduct an investigation and evaluate the experimental design to provide evidence that fields exist between objects exerting forces on each other even though the objects are not in contact.

MS-PS3-2 Develop a model to describe that when the arrangement of objects interacting at a distance changes, different amounts of potential energy are stored in the system.

Connect It !

✏ **Magnetic field lines represent the invisible force around a magnet. Trace one of the magnetic field lines on this page.**

Translate Information How can you describe the shape of Earth's magnetic field?

....

SEP Use Models What does the model show about Earth's magnetic field?

....

....

SEP Define Problems What is a limitation of this two-dimensional model?

....

Magnetic Force and Energy

You may use magnets to display notes or pictures on the door of your refrigerator. A **magnet** attracts iron and materials that contain iron. Magnets can be any size, from the ones you use in the kitchen to the entire Earth and beyond. People can use magnetic compasses in navigation because the magnetic effect on a compass needle is predictable. The planet Earth is a natural system that acts as a magnet (**Figure 1**).

Magnets attract iron and some other materials—usually metals. They attract or repel other magnets. This attraction or repulsion is called **magnetism**. The **interaction** between a magnet and a substance containing iron is always an attraction. Magnets themselves can either attract or repel one another, depending on how they are placed.

Magnetism can be permanent or temporary. Some materials, containing iron or certain other metals, can become permanent magnets after interacting with other magnets. Temporary magnetism, on the other hand, can occur in different ways. An iron or steel object that is touching a magnet can become a magnet itself as long as the contact continues. For example, you can make a chain of paper clips that hangs from a permanent magnet. Another type of temporary magnet is created when an electric current flows through a conductor. This kind of magnet exists as long as the current is flowing.

Academic Vocabulary

Student Discourse The term *interaction* comes from words meaning *action* and *between two* things. Discuss with a classmate an interaction that you had today.

....

....

....

Magnetic Force

Figure 1 Lines and arrows show the direction of the magnetic field around Earth.

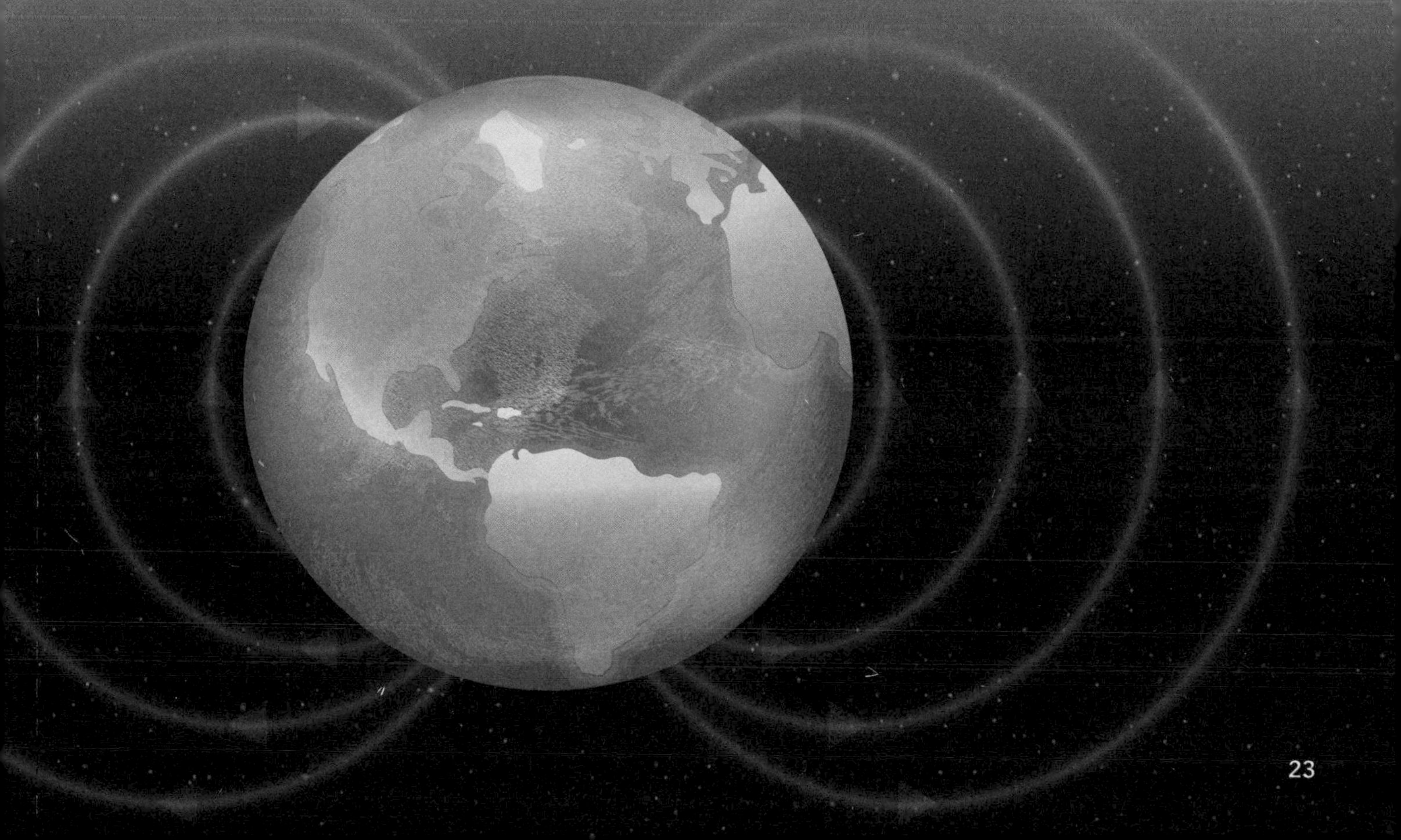

23

Magnetic Force

Magnetic Force Magnetism is caused by a force that can act at a distance. This **magnetic force** is a push or pull that occurs when a magnet interacts with another object. Some large magnets can attract objects from many meters away and are powerful enough to lift a car or truck. The magnetic force transfers kinetic energy to those objects.

How do you know if the magnetic force between two objects will be a push or a pull? A magnet exerts a pull on a magnetic object that is not itself a magnet. If you place the ends of the horseshoe magnet in **Figure 2** near a pile of paper clips, the paper clips always move toward the magnet. They never move away. Every magnet has two ends, called **magnetic poles**, where the magnetic force is strongest. One pole is known as the *north pole* and the other is known as the *south pole*.

The arrangement of magnets determines which type of force exists between them. If you bring two magnets together so that *like* poles—either both north or both south—are near each other, the magnets repel. If you bring the magnets together so that opposite poles are close to one another, the magnets attract. **Figure 2** shows two ways in which bar magnets can interact.

Push or Pull

Figure 2 ✏ SEP Develop Models Magnets can either push or pull. Draw arrows on the paperclips and on the bar magnets to show the direction of the magnetic force.

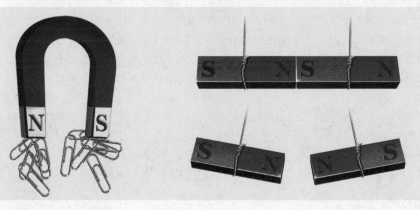

Magnets and Potential Energy

Magnets and Potential Energy Recall the ways in which the potential energy of a system of electric charges can change. As you apply a force to move opposite charges away from each other, the electrical potential energy of the system increases. The same is true of magnets. Opposite poles naturally attract each other, so you must put energy into the system to pull them apart. As you apply a force to separate the two opposite poles, the potential energy of the system increases. When the magnetic force between opposite poles pulls them together, the potential energy of the system decreases. On the other hand, like poles repel each other. To push them together, you have to transfer energy to the system. This increases the potential energy of the system. Use the **Figure 3** activity to summarize these changes in potential energy.

HANDS-ON LAB

ⅢⅠ**Investigate** Discover how you can use a magnet to tell the difference between real and fake coins.

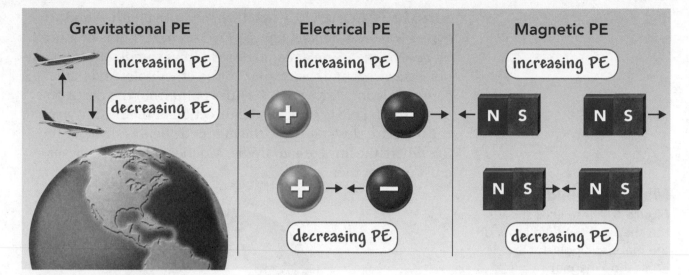

Gravitational PE

increasing PE

decreasing PE

Electrical PE

increasing PE

decreasing PE

Magnetic PE

increasing PE

decreasing PE

Magnetic Fields

The magnetic force is strongest at a magnet's poles. That is why the paper clips tend to stick to the horseshoe magnet at its ends. There is an area of magnetic force that surrounds a magnet. This area of force is the **magnetic field** of the magnet. This field contains magnetic energy. It allows magnets to attract objects at a distance. The magnetic field extends from one pole to the other pole of the magnet. You cannot see a magnetic field, but if you place tiny pieces of iron near a magnet, they will arrange themselves along the magnetic field. Their arrangement looks much like lines, so illustrations of magnetic fields are drawn with lines, as shown in **Figure 4**.

Objects containing iron, such as steel paper clips, experience a force when they are in a magnetic field. These objects line up with the field around them. Particles inside the objects can also line up with the field. When the particles in an object line up with the field, the object becomes a temporary magnet.

Potential Energy
Figure 3 The gravitational force between the plane and Earth is an attractive force. The forces between opposite charges and opposite magnetic poles are also attractive. Label the systems of objects with increasing and decreasing potential energy in the diagrams.

Visualizing Magnetic Fields
Figure 4 The magnetic field around a bar magnet causes iron filings to form the arrangement shown. This arrangement can also be represented with magnetic field lines. The field is strongest where the lines are closest together.

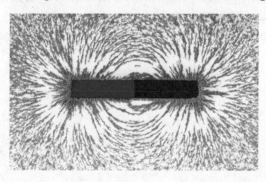

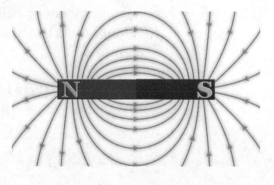

Single Magnetic Field The lines in **Figure 4** and **Figure 5** show a single magnetic field—a field that is produced by one magnet. Single magnetic field lines spread out from one pole, curve around the magnet to the other pole, and make complete loops. Arrows on the lines point from the north pole to the south pole to indicate the direction of the field. When the lines are close together, the magnetic field is stronger than it is where the lines are far apart. Magnetic field lines never cross one another.

Magnetic Field Lines

Figure 5 These lines show the shape of the field around the magnetic poles of a horseshoe magnet.

1. Claim Add labels to the illustration to show where the magnetic field is strongest and where it is weakest.

2. Evidence What is the relationship between distance from the magnet and the strength of its magnetic field?

....

....

....

3. Reasoning Could you pick up a nail using the curved part of the horseshoe magnet farthest from the poles? Explain your answer.

....

....

....

....

....

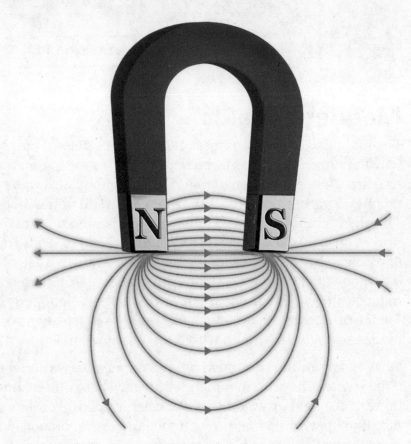

Combined Magnetic Field The magnetic fields of two magnets placed close together will interact with each other. When two like poles are close together, the poles and the magnetic fields around them repel one another. When two opposite poles are close together, the fields combine to form a strong magnetic field between the two magnets, as shown in **Figure 6**. As in a single magnetic field, the lines never cross one another.

☑ **CHECK POINT** **Identify** What does the distance between magnetic field lines indicate?

....

....

Combined Magnetic Field Lines

Figure 6 The image on the left shows the combined magnetic field when opposite poles of bar magnets face each other.

SEP Develop Models What would the magnetic field look like if like poles faced each other?

✎ Draw a model of the magnetic field lines in the image on the right.

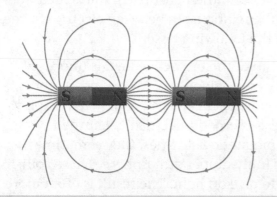

Earth's Magnetic Field

Earth itself acts as a very large magnet. Materials in the core of the planet generate a magnetic field that surrounds the planet. This magnetic field is very similar to the field that surrounds a bar magnet. The magnetic poles of Earth are located near the geographic poles. These are the points where the magnetic field is strongest. The magnetic field lines pass out of the core and through the rocky mantle. They also loop through the space surrounding Earth. The magnetic field is three-dimensional and it is shaped like a donut, as shown in **Figure 7**.

People have used this magnetic field for many centuries for navigation. A compass, shown in **Figure 7**, is a magnetized needle that can turn easily. The needle interacts with Earth's magnetic field. One end is attracted to the north magnetic pole and the other end to the south magnetic pole. People can use a compass to determine the direction in which they are traveling.

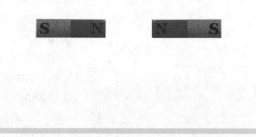

▶ **VIDEO**

See how magnetic fields interact.

Compass

Figure 7 Sailors and hikers use a compass to determine direction. The needle always points toward the magnetic north pole. This is the pole that we call the North Pole, but because it is actually a south magnetic pole, the magnetic field lines point toward it.

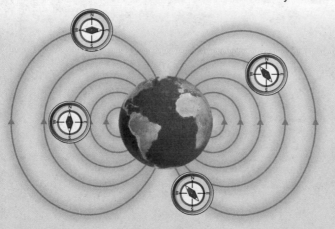

Literacy Connection

Verify Use a reliable Internet source to verify that Earth's magnetic field is caused by substances inside the planet. Which source did you use? How do you know that it's reliable?

....

....

....

....

Aurora Borealis

Figure 8 These rare red aurora over Mono Lake, California, form when Earth's magnetic field pushes charged particles toward the poles. The high-energy particles interact with molecules in the atmosphere.

Protecting Life on Earth There is a constant stream of particles that flows from the sun toward Earth. This stream is known as the *solar wind*. These particles have electric charges and they have high energy as they move very rapidly through space. If they were to reach the surface of Earth, the particles in the stream could harm living things. Fortunately, Earth's magnetic field protects organisms. Electrically charged particles in motion interact with magnetic forces. Earth's magnetic field changes the motion of the charged particles. They flow toward the north and south poles and then past Earth into space. You will learn more about the relationship between electric charges and magnetic fields in the following lessons.

Although the mechanism of the protective field is unobservable, you can sometimes see evidence of it working. Auroras, sometimes called the "Northern Lights," are glowing displays in the night sky. As these energetic electrically charged particles travel along the magnetic field lines, they sometimes collide with gas atoms in the upper atmosphere. These collisions cause the atoms to give off light. The result is often more spectacular than a fireworks show (**Figure 8**).

☑ **CHECK POINT** **Cite Textual Evidence** Describe how the aurora borealis is evidence that Earth has a magnetic field.

....

....

....

....

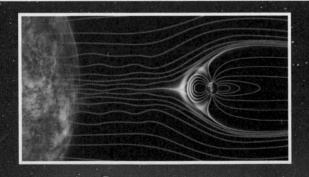

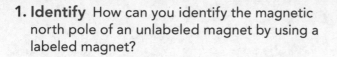

MS-PS2-5, MS-PS3-2

1. Identify How can you identify the magnetic north pole of an unlabeled magnet by using a labeled magnet?

....

....

....

....

2. CCC Patterns How would increasing the strength of the field of a magnet change the pattern of magnetic field lines between its poles?

....

....

3. Apply Concepts Explain how potential energy changes when you pull a magnet off a refrigerator door.

....

....

....

....

4. SEP Construct Explanations Why is the electrical charge on particles in the solar wind an important element of the protection that Earth's magnetic field provides?

....

....

....

5. SEP Develop Models ✏ Draw the magnetic field lines around a nail that has its head as its north pole and its point as its south pole.

In this lesson, you discovered magnetic fields and how to draw the lines that represent them. You also learned how potential energy changes when a magnet is present.

SEP Design Solutions Describe the technical tasks you would perform to orient two magnets so that they repel each other. How might this apply to your levitation device? What data would show that your device could work?

....

....

....

....

....

HANDS-ON LAB

Tracking Levitation

Go online to download the lab worksheet. You will consider how a stable train and section of track can be built using permanent magnets.

HANDS-ON LAB

⋃Investigate Explore the relationship between electricity and magnetism.

MS-PS2-3 Ask questions about data to determine the factors that affect the strength of electric and magnetic forces.

Connect It !

✏ **Circle the magnet in the photo.**

SEP Interpret Data How do you know that the object picking up the metal beams is a magnet?

....

....

SEP Construct Explanations What material do you think makes up this magnet?

....

Electromagnetic Principles

Have a look at **Figure 1**. How is this crane's magnet strong enough to lift these heavy metal beams? The answer may surprise you. The magnetic field of this crane is actually generated by an electric current! The relationship between electricity and magnetism is called **electromagnetism**.

Electromagnetism was first discovered by a scientist named Hans Christian Ørsted. During a class he was teaching, he brought a compass near a wire that had an electric current running through it. He noticed that the compass needle changed direction when it was near the wire. He placed several different compasses near a wire and found out that the compass needles changed direction when a current passed through the wire. The compass needles did not change direction when no current flowed. Ørsted concluded that an electric current produces a magnetic field, so electricity and magnetism are related.

Literacy Connection

Cite Textual Evidence
Analyze the text in detail to explain the evidence that Ørsted used to support his conclusion that an electric current produces a magnetic field.

....

....

....

....

....

Write About It In your science notebook, describe a time that you drew a new conclusion from your observations.

Magnetic Strength
Figure 1 A regular magnet is not strong enough to pick up these heavy rails. This special type of magnet, called an *electromagnet*, has the strength to do it.

Magnetism from Electricity

Figure 2 ✏️ **Predict Phenomena** In this figure, you see two systems designed to show how the direction of a current in a straight wire affects the magnetic field that forms. In the system on the left, the current flows upward. Draw your predicted magnetic field lines for the system on the right, in which the current flows downward.

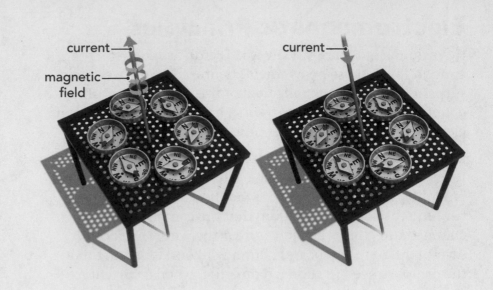

current ⟶
magnetic field

current ⟶

HANDS-ON LAB

🧪 **Investigate** Explore the relationship between electricity and magnetism.

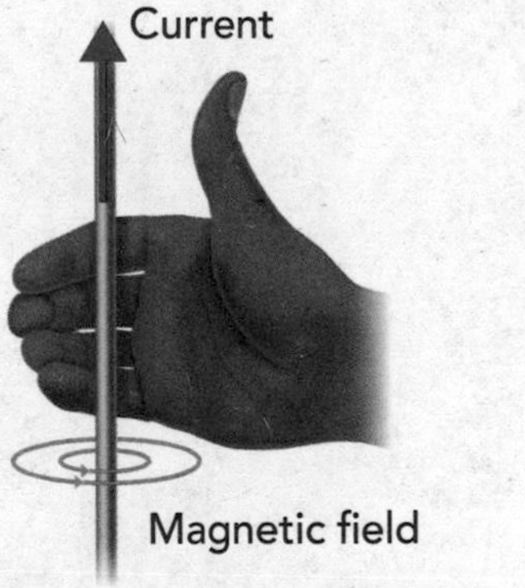

Current

Magnetic field

The Right-Hand Rule

Figure 3 Imagine that you are holding the wire in your right hand with your thumb pointing in the direction the current flows. The direction of the magnetic field is the same as the direction that your fingers curl.

Magnetic Fields and Current

When you examine **Figure 2**, you can see that the magnetic field produced by a current has a certain direction. This field also has a certain strength. How can the field change? It can change in direction and strength, and it can be turned off or on. To turn the magnetic field off or on, simply turn the current off or on.

Magnetic Fields Around Straight Wires In a straight wire, the field's direction depends on the direction of the current. How do you determine the direction of a magnetic field based on the direction of current through a straight wire? You can use what is known as the right-hand rule, as shown in **Figure 3**.

To change the strength of a magnetic field around a current-carrying straight wire, change the amount of current running through the wire. If current is increased, the magnetic field becomes stronger. If the current is decreased, the strength of the magnetic field decreases.

✅ CHECK POINT **Determine Central Ideas** How do electric currents relate to magnetic fields?

....

....

Magnetic Fields Around Wire Loops

Suppose you have a loop of wire rather than a straight wire. The magnetic field formed around the loop of wire is in many ways like the field formed when a current flows through a straight wire. The direction of the field depends on the direction of the current and can be determined by using the right-hand rule. The field can be turned off or on by turning the current off or on. The strength of the field depends on the strength of the current.

There is an important difference, however, when a current flows through a loop of wire. Look at **Figure 4**, which shows a current flowing through a loop of wire and the magnetic field it produces. Shaping a wire into a loop can increase the strength of the magnetic field within the loop.

✔ CHECK POINT **Predict Phenomena** You have a straight wire with a current running through it. You change the system by looping the wire. What effect will the change have on the magnetic field?

Model It

Magnetic Field Strength

Figure 4 The overhead view of a magnetic field formed by a current flowing through a single wire is shown. The magnetic field lines are closest together in the center of the loop, where the magnetic field is stronger. The number of loops in a wire controls the strength of a magnetic field.

1. SEP Develop Models ✏ Draw the magnetic field lines around the two stacked loops of wire.

2. SEP Use Models Is the strength of the magnetic field inside the loop greater or less than the strength when there was just one loop of wire? Justify your answer.

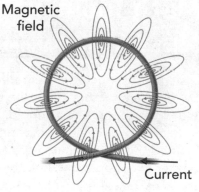

Magnetic field

Current

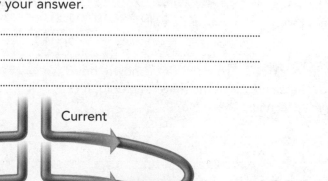

Current

INTERACTIVITY

Predict the direction of magnetic field lines around a current-carrying wire.

Solenoids and Electromagnets

There are many practical uses of coiling a current-carrying wire to make a strong magnetic field. Two devices that strengthen a magnetic field by running a current through coiled wire are solenoids and electromagnets. A **solenoid** is a coil of wire with a current running through it, as shown in **Figure 5**. It is just stacked loops of wire. In a solenoid, the magnetic field is strengthened in the center of the coil when a current runs through the coil. One end of a solenoid acts like the north pole of a magnet, and the other end acts like the south pole.

Solenoids

Figure 5 The image shows the magnetic field lines around a solenoid.
Reason Abstractly The diagram shows that field lines spread out as you move away from the magnet. Do the spreading lines show that the magnetic force gets stronger or gets weaker with increasing distance?

....

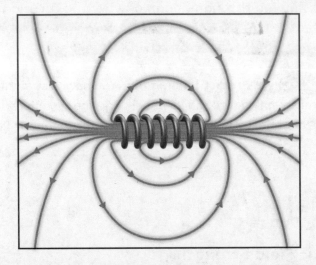

Math Toolbox

Solenoids and Magnetic Fields

A scientist conducted an experiment to investigate how different factors affect the strength of a magnetic field in the center of a solenoid. The solenoid was made of iron wire. In the experiment, the scientist changed the current passing through the wire and the number of coils per unit length of the solenoid. The results of the experiment are shown in the table. A *tesla* is the SI unit for the strength of a magnetic field.

Number of Coils per meter	Current (amp)	Magnetic Field Strength (tesla)
100	1	20,000
200	1	40,000
100	2	40,000
200	2	80,000

1. **Draw Comparative Inferences** From the data shown, how does the current affect the strength of the magnetic field, if the number of coils per meter remains the same?

....

....

2. **SEP Interpret Data** From the data shown, how does the number of coils per meter affect the strength of the magnetic field, if current is constant?

....

....

Field Strength and Solenoids

You can increase the strength of the magnetic field inside a solenoid by winding the coils closer together. As in a straight wire, increasing the current through the solenoid wire will also increase the magnetic field.

INTERACTIVITY

Apply your knowledge of electromagnets and factors that affect electromagnetic force.

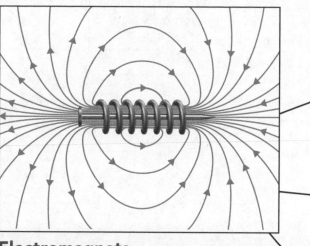

Electromagnets

Figure 6 A solenoid with a nail in the core is a simple electromagnet. More advanced electromagnets have many practical uses.

Some doors are locked with electromagnets and can only be unlocked electronically.

Electromagnets are used both to lift this train off the track and to propel it forward.

Electromagnets

What else can you do to a solenoid to make the magnetic field even stronger? You add a ferromagnetic material to it. A ferromagnetic material is a substance that becomes a magnet when exposed to a magnetic field. The elements iron, nickel, and cobalt are ferromagnetic. As shown in **Figure 6**, a solenoid with a ferromagnetic core is called an **electromagnet**. When a ferromagnetic material is placed within a solenoid, both the current and the magnetized material **produce** a magnetic field. This combination produces a magnetic field that is stronger than that produced by the solenoid alone. As in a solenoid, the magnetic field of an electromagnet increases when the closeness of the coils or the current increases.

Think back to the electromagnet you saw in **Figure 1**. How might you get the electromagnet to drop the metal rails? Just as with other magnetic fields caused by currents, you turn off the current. The magnetic field no longer exists, and the rails drop. Some other uses for electromagnets are shown in **Figure 6**.

☑ CHECK POINT **Summarize** What is the difference between a solenoid and an electromagnet?

An electromagnet helps to produce the vibrations in these headphones. These vibrations carry sound to your ears.

Academic Vocabulary

The term *produce* has several meanings. What does it mean in the text on this page?

....

....

1. Explain What did Ørsted discover about electricity and magnetism?

....

....

2. CCC Cause and Effect Suppose that an electric current flows in a straight wire. You change the system so that the current flows in the opposite direction. Predict what changes will occur in the magnetic field, and what will stay the same.

....

....

....

3. SEP Develop Models 🖊 A straight wire has a current running through it. Draw the current-carrying wire and the magnetic field that it produces.

4. Compare and Contrast Compare and contrast a solenoid and an electromagnet. What do they have in common? How are they different?

....

....

....

....

....

....

....

....

....

5. SEP Engage in Argument An MRI machine uses an electromagnet to obtain scans of the human body. It uses these scans to generate images. What advantage is there in using an electromagnet instead of a solenoid in an MRI machine?

....

....

....

Quest CHECK-IN

In this lesson, you learned about electromagnetism and how electric currents generate magnetic fields. You also discovered how solenoids and electromagnets increase the strength of the magnetic fields.

SEP Evaluate Information How might you apply the principles of electromagnetism when building your levitating device?

....

....

....

....

HANDS-ON LAB

Building an Electromagnet

Go online to download the lab worksheet. Build an electromagnetic and determine how to control the strength of the electromagnetic force.

MS-PS2-3

ELECTROMAGNETISM In Action

▶ VIDEO

Explore examples of electromagnetism.

How can you combine electric and magnetic forces to play a game or accomplish a task? You engineer it!

The Challenge: To engineer devices that rely on elecromagnetic force

Phenomenon People have known for centuries that electricity sparks and that magnets attract. The magnetic compass, for example, has been used since at least the 1200s, and possibly a great deal longer. But it was only in modern times that scientists and engineers began to understand that electricity and magnetism could affect each other.

Electromagnets differ from ordinary magnets because they only attract or repel when an electric current runs through them. An engineer can control an electromagnet, making it useful in industrial applications.

Electromagnetics govern a wide variety of devices and games, from a simple pinball machine to the Large Hadron Collider, an underground experimental facility for studying the forces of nature. Hospitals use electromagnetics in procedures such as magnetic resonance imaging (MRI). The music industry has found many uses for electromagnets—in speakers, headphones, complex percussion instruments, and recording equipment. Transportation is another field that makes extensive use of electromagnetic technology. The high-speed maglev trains use electromagnetic force to hover above the track and whisk passengers to their destinations at speeds as great as 600 kilometers per hour.

MRI and pinball machines are just two examples of the many devices that use electromagnets!

DESIGN CHALLENGE What can you design and build with an electromagnet? Go to the Engineering Design Notebook to find out!

Electric and Magnetic Interactions

HANDS-ON LAB

Investigate Discover the factors that affect the strength of electric and magnetic forces in a motor.

MS-PS2-3 Ask questions about data to determine the factors that affect the strength of electric and magnetic forces.

Connect It

✏️ **Circle the part of the image that shows that electrical energy has been transformed into mechanical energy.**

SEP Construct Explanations Explain how you think the trolley works.

....

....

Identify List two other examples in which electrical energy transforms into mechanical energy.

....

....

Magnetic Force on Moving Charges

If a charged particle is at rest in a magnetic field, it is not affected by the field. But if the charged particle moves, it experiences a magnetic force. Why does this happen?

Recall that electric current is charged particles in motion. Suppose you have a wire with a current flowing through it, and you place it at rest in a magnetic field between two magnets. In this situation, there are two magnetic fields at play. The first field is caused by the magnets. The second field is caused by the current flowing through the wire. The magnetic field of the magnets interacts with the magnetic field around the wire. This interaction results in a force on the wire and causes the wire to move in the same direction as the force. The resulting force on the wire is perpendicular to the magnetic field, as given by another right-hand rule. This right-hand rule explains the direction of the force that a current-carrying wire in a magnetic field, as shown in **Figure 1**.

How does the trolley in **Figure 2** work? Inside the trolley is an electric motor. The motor uses interactions between magnetic fields generated by loops of wire and magnetic fields of magnets. To understand how the motor works, take a look at how a current-carrying loop of wire is affected by a magnetic field.

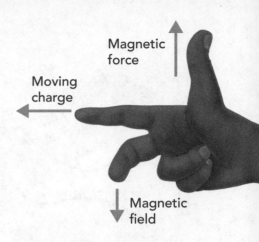

Magnetic force

Moving charge

Magnetic field

Right-Hand Rule #2
Figure 1 Point your index finger in the direction of the current, and bend your middle finger so that it points in the direction of the magnetic field. Your thumb points in the direction of the magnetic force on the moving charges.

Transforming into Mechanical Energy
Figure 2 The wheels of this trolley in San Diego, California, move when current flows into the trolley.

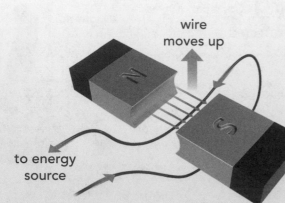

wire
moves up

to energy
source

to energy
source

wire
rotates

Current in a Magnetic Field

Figure 3 A straight wire moves in one direction in a magnetic field. A loop of wire rotates.

Loop of Current in a Magnetic Field

If a straight wire with a current through it moves in the direction of the force on it, what happens when that wire forms a loop? Compare the two situations in **Figure 3**. When a single wire of current is placed in a magnetic field, it moves in one direction. But when a loop of current is placed in that same field, it rotates. The current flows in one direction on one side of the loop. On the other side of the loop, the current flows in the opposite direction. As a result, the magnetic force on one side of the loop points up, and on the other side, the force points down. Because of the directions of these forces, the loop does not rotate in a complete circle. It rotates only half a turn, moving from horizontal to vertical.

Galvanometers

This type of rotation is the basis of a **galvanometer**, which is a device that measures small currents. Showing how much current is flowing has many uses, such as in fuel gauges or medical sensors. **Figure 4** shows a galvanometer. In this device, an electromagnet is suspended between two permanent magnets and is attached to the needle of the galvanometer. Recall that one way the strength of an electromagnet is determined is by the amount of current supplied to it. In a galvanometer, the current supplied to the electromagnet is the current that is being measured. If the current is extremely small, the force created is also small, and the needle rotates only a small amount. For a larger current, the force is greater, and the needle moves more.

Galvanometer

Figure 4 An electromagnet in the galvanometer turns the pointer to indicate the amount of current present. Why does an electromagnet act like a loop of wire in a magnetic field?

....

....

....

Electric Motors An **electric motor** is a device that uses an electric current to turn an axle. In doing that, it transforms electrical energy into mechanical energy.

Examine **Figure 5** to learn the parts that make up an electric motor and how they work together to produce mechanical energy. Recall that a simple loop of wire in a magnetic field can only rotate half a turn because the current flows in only one direction. However, connecting the loop (also called the *armature*) to a commutator and brushes allows the current to change direction, as shown in **Figure 5**. Each time the commutator moves to a different brush, the current flows in the opposite direction. Thus, the side of the armature that just moved up will now move down, and the armature rotates continuously in one direction. Just picture the armature of a motor attached to an axle to which the blades of a fan are connected. Start the current, and feel the breeze!

☑ CHECK POINT **Determine Differences** What is the only part of a motor through which a current does not flow?

VIDEO
See what it's like to be an electrical engineer.

HANDS-ON LAB

✏️**Investigate** Discover the factors that affect the strength of electric and magnetic forces in a motor.

How a Motor Works
Figure 5 ✏️ A motor is made of several basic parts, each of which is described below. Study the information about each part. Then, write the number of each description in the appropriate circle on the image.

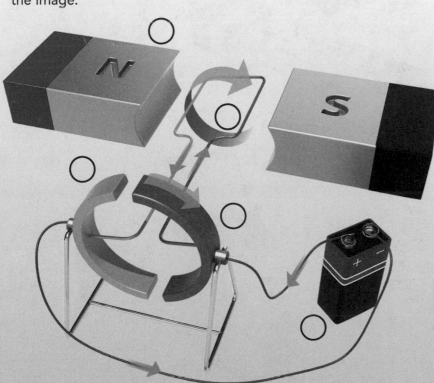

1. Permanent magnets produce a magnetic field. This causes the armature to turn when current flows. Magnets with stronger fields will make the armature turn faster.

2. The **commutator** consists to two semicircular pieces of metal. It conducts current from the brushes to the armature.

3. Brushes, which do not move, conduct current to the commutator.

4. The **armature** is a loop of wire that current flows through. A real motor has an armature with dozens or hundreds of loops.

5. The **battery** is the energy source that supplies the current to the brushes.

41

Electromagnetic Induction

You've seen how a current flowing through a wire produces a magnetic field, and how electrical energy can be transformed into mechanical energy. The scientist Michael Faraday discovered that the opposite is also possible. A magnetic field can be used to produce a current. If a conductor is moving through a magnetic field, a current is generated in the conductor. **Electromagnetic induction** is the process of generating an electric current from the motion of a conductor through a magnetic field. In this case, mechanical energy is transformed into electrical energy. The resulting current is called an *induced current*.

Induced Current and Moving Conductors

By experimentation, scientists discovered that when a conductor is moved in a magnetic field, a current flows through the conductor. Current can be induced if the conductor is a straight wire, as shown in **Figure 6**. The same principle applies if the conductor is a coil of wire. Induced current is present any time that a conductor moves through a magnetic field.

Literacy Connection

Draw Evidence Underline the sentence in the text that identifies the transformation of energy that occurs during electromagnetic induction.

▶ VIDEO

Watch electromagnetic induction in action.

Induction from a Moving Wire

Figure 6 When a conductor (such as a metal wire) moves through a magnetic field, current will be induced in the conductor.

SEP Interpret Data Examine the image. Then use the term *clockwise* or *counterclockwise* to complete each sentence correctly.

When the conductor moves upward through the magnetic field, the induced current flows _____.
When the conductor moves downward, the induced current is _____.

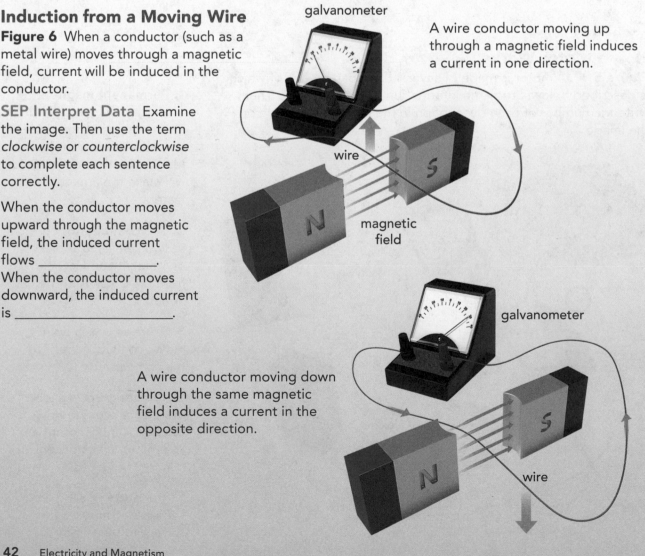

galvanometer

A wire conductor moving up through a magnetic field induces a current in one direction.

wire

magnetic field

galvanometer

A wire conductor moving down through the same magnetic field induces a current in the opposite direction.

wire

Induced Current and Moving Magnets As you
have read, an electric current is induced when a conductor
moves through a magnetic field. A current also is induced when
a magnet moves through a loop of conductive wire. Examine
Figure 7, which shows what happens when a magnet moves
through a loop of wire.

In summary, electric current is induced in a conductor whenever
the magnetic field around the conductor is changing. When
a conductor is in a magnetic field, a current is induced in the
conductor whenever either the conductor or the magnetic field
is moving.

☑CHECK POINT **Integrate with Visuals** Based on Figure 6 and
Figure 7, what are the two ways that a magnetic field can change,
relative to a conductor?

....

....

....

Induction from a Moving Magnet
Figure 7 Current will be induced in a conductor
in a magnetic field when the magnetic field
moves in relation to the conductor.

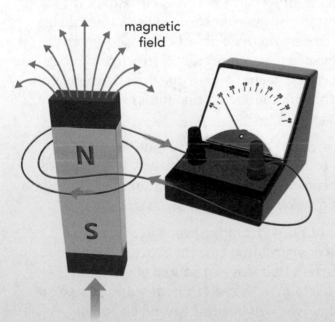

magnetic field

magnet moves up

A magnetic field moving up through
a wire conductor induces a current in
one direction.

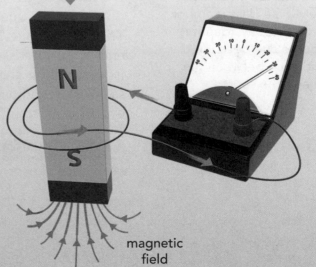

magnet moves down

A magnetic field moving
down through a wire
conductor induces a current
in the opposite direction.

magnetic field

Question It!

Types of Current

Figure 8 It is not uncommon for one system to require both direct and alternating currents to operate.

SEP Ask Questions Most families don't own one, but there are more than 40,000 electric cars registered in California. They are becoming part of your everyday environment. Perhaps you have studied them in your classroom or seen them in museums. Did you know that an electric car uses both AC and DC? Write a question about the use of AC and DC in the car.

Alternating and Direct Current

Alternating and Direct Current You probably know that not all electric currents are alike. The type of current that comes from a battery is direct current. Direct current, or DC, has charges that flow in only one direction. Objects that run on batteries use direct current. In these objects, opposite ends of the battery are connected to opposite ends of the circuit. When everything is connected, current flows in one direction from one end of the battery, through the circuit, and into the other end of the battery.

The other type of current is alternating current. Alternating current, or AC, is a constantly reversing current. When a wire in a magnetic field constantly changes direction, the induced current it produces also keeps changing direction.

Alternating current has an advantage over direct current, because the voltage of alternating current is easily changed. For example, the current that leaves a **source** of electrical power has voltage too high to be used in homes and businesses. The high voltage, however, can be used to send electrical energy hundreds of miles away from its source. When it reaches its destination, the voltage can be reduced to a level that is safe for use in homes and other places. Use **Figure 8** to further examine AC and DC.

✓ CHECK POINT **Determine Central Ideas** What is the main difference between AC and DC?

Generators and Transformers

Two common and important devices that use induced current are generators and transformers. Generators and transformers are alike in that an electrical current leaves both of them. They differ in that generators produce electricity, and transformers change the voltage to make the electricity useful.

How Generators Work An electric generator transforms mechanical energy into an electric current. Although a generator contains many of the same parts as an electric motor, the two devices work in reverse. In an electric motor, an existing current produces a magnetic field, and electrical energy is transformed into mechanical energy. In a generator, the motion of a coil of wire through a magnetic field produces a current, and mechanical energy is transformed into electrical energy.

A DC generator is the same as the motor you saw in **Figure 5.** If you turn the armature, mechanical energy is converted to electrical energy. An AC generator is very similar, but it has slip rings instead of a commutator. **Figure 9** shows the slip rings as well as the armature, magnets, brushes, and crank. It also shows how they work together to produce an alternating current. The basic operation of a small home generator is the same as that of a large generator that provides current to many homes and businesses.

INTERACTIVITY

Construct a virtual generator that can charge a cell phone.

INTERACTIVITY

Explore how electricity and magnetism affect the motion of various materials.

How a Generator Works

Figure 9 ✏ An AC generator works when its component parts operate together. Number the part names in the correct order to show the operation of a generator from the magnets to the moment when the current is produced. Then, circle the names of the parts of the generator that you would also find in an electric motor.

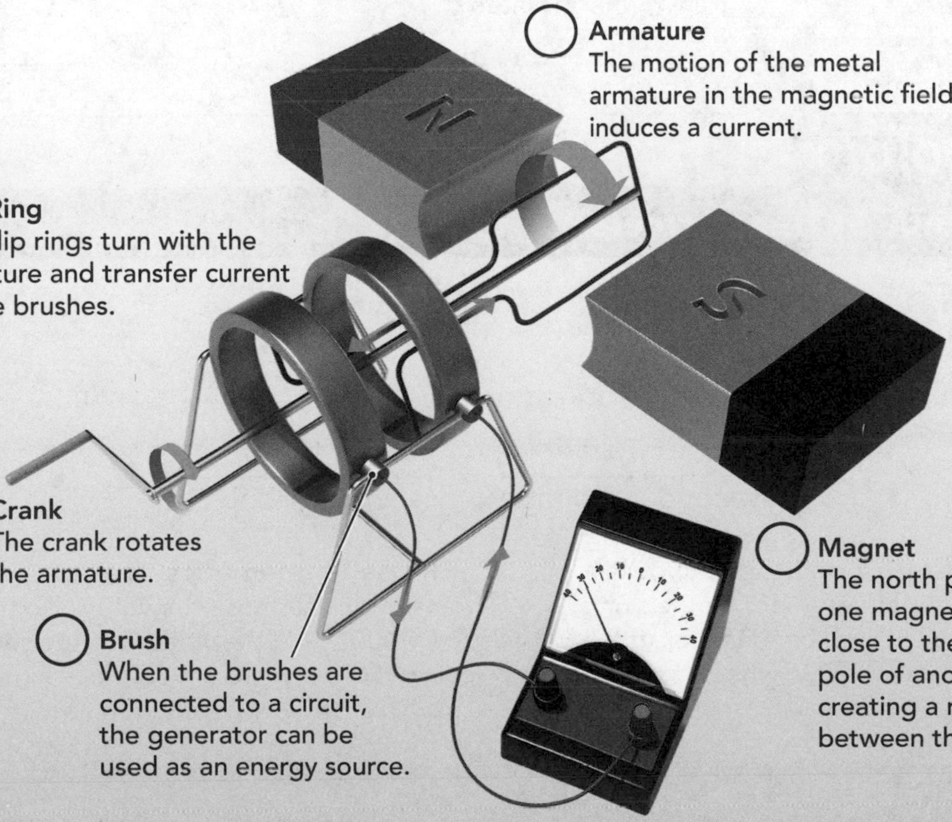

○ **Armature**
The motion of the metal armature in the magnetic field induces a current.

○ **Slip Ring**
The slip rings turn with the armature and transfer current to the brushes.

○ **Crank**
The crank rotates the armature.

○ **Brush**
When the brushes are connected to a circuit, the generator can be used as an energy source.

○ **Magnet**
The north pole of one magnet is placed close to the south pole of another magnet, creating a magnetic field between them.

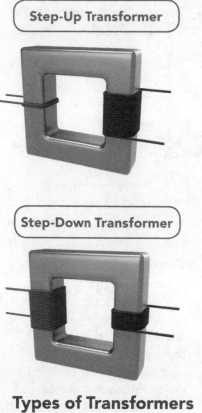

Step-Up Transformer

Step-Down Transformer

Types of Transformers

Figure 10 In step-up transformers, the primary coil has fewer loops than the secondary coil. In step-down transformers, the primary coil has more loops.

How Transformers Work

You have probably heard the word *transformer* before, but you may not know what an electrical transformer is. This type of **transformer** is a device that increases or decreases voltage using two separate coils of insulated wire that are wrapped around an iron core.

The first coil that the current goes through is called the *primary coil*. This coil is connected to a circuit with an alternating current voltage source. The other coil is called the *secondary coil*. It is connected to a circuit, but it does not have a voltage source. The coils share an iron core. Because the primary coil is connected to alternating current, the direction of the current constantly changes. As a result, the magnetic field around it also changes, and it induces a current in the secondary coil. The current in the secondary coil depends on the number of loops in the coil.

There are two types of transformers. As shown in **Figure 10**, the type depends on which coil has more loops. Step-up transformers, such as those used to help transmit electricity from generating plants, increase voltage. Step-down transformers, such as those used in phone chargers, decrease voltage. The phone charger reduces the voltage to what is needed to charge a cell phone. The greater the ratio between the numbers of loops in the primary and secondary coils in a transformer, the more the voltage will change.

✓ CHECK POINT **Summarize Text** How are generators and transformers related?

....

....

Math Toolbox

Voltage Change in Transformers

The equation shows that the ratio of voltage in the two coils is equal to the ratio of loops.

$$\frac{\text{primary voltage}}{\text{secondary voltage}} = \frac{\text{primary loops}}{\text{secondary loops}}$$

1. **Understand Ratio Concepts** Suppose a step-up transformer has 1 loop in the primary coil and 8 loops in the secondary coil. If the secondary voltage is 120 V, what must be the primary voltage? Show your work.

....

....

2. **SEP Use Mathematics** In a step-down transformer, suppose the voltage in the primary coil is 600 V and the voltage in the secondary coil is 150 V. If there are 36 loops in the primary coil, how many loops are in the secondary coil?

....

....

☑ LESSON 4 Check

1. **SEP Use Mathematics** Suppose the secondary voltage of a transformer is 60 V, and there are 40 loops on the primary coil and 120 loops on the secondary coil. What is the primary voltage of the transformer? Show your work.

2. **Compare and Contrast** How are electric motors and generators similar? How are they different?

....

....

....

....

....

....

3. **SEP Construct Explanations** In many areas electricity is produced by huge generators close to dams. What function does large volumes of moving water have in generating electricity?

....

....

....

....

....

4. **SEP Develop Models** Suppose you build model airplanes. Use what you know from this lesson to draw a model of a device that would keep a propeller turning as the plane flew.

Quest CHECK-IN

In this lesson, you discovered that an electric charge in motion experiences a magnetic force in a magnetic field. You also learned how charges can be set in motion within a conductor by moving the conductor through a magnetic field and that a moving magnetic field can induce a current through a wire. Additionally, you discovered how motors, generators, and transformers work.

Apply Concepts How might a motor, generator, or transformer be used as part of your levitation device?

....

....

HANDS-ON LAB

Electrifying Levitation

Go online to download the lab worksheet. Test your levitation device and see how an optimal design can be achieved.

🕐 MS-PS2-3, MS-PS2-5, MS-PS3-2

Evidence-Based Assessment

Manny is investigating factors that affect electric and magnetic forces. He needs to design an experiment to show that objects can exert forces on each other even when they are not in direct contact.

After doing some additional research, Manny decides to make an electromagnet with a battery, some wire, an iron nail, and a switch. He uses a rubber eraser as an insulator to open and close the switch. He uses the electromagnet to see if he can pick up some paperclips.

The diagram shows the setup of Manny's experiment.

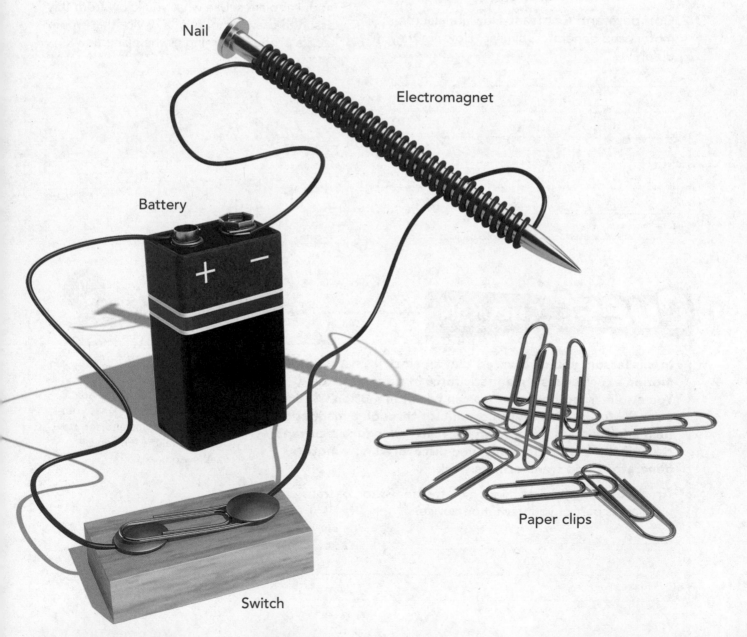

Nail

Electromagnet

Battery

+ −

Paper clips

Switch

1. **SEP Analyze Data** What is one of the benefits of Manny's electromagnet?
   A. It can only repel objects.
   B. It produces a current through electromagnetic induction.
   C. The magnetic field can be turned on and off.
   D. Its strength cannot be changed.

2. **CCC Cause and Effect** What could Manny do to increase the strength of the electromagnetic force? Select all that apply.
   ☐ Increase the number of coils around the nail.
   ☐ Increase the current by using a battery with a greater voltage.
   ☐ Decrease the number of coils around the nail.
   ☐ Decrease the current by using a battery with a smaller voltage.

3. **SEP Cite Evidence** What evidence is there that the electromagnet exerts a force on the paper clips, even though they are not touching each other? Circle the words that make the statements true.

   The electromagnetic force of the electromagnet (attracts / repels) the paper clips. The paper clips move (toward / away) from the nail.

4. **CCC Analyze Systems** Manny detaches the two wires from the battery and reattaches them to the opposite terminals. Explain how this changes the current and magnetic field.

   ....
   ....
   ....
   ....
   ....
   ....

5. **SEP Explain Phenomena** Suppose you pull the paper clips away from the nail. Explain how the potential energy of the system changes.

   ....
   ....
   ....
   ....
   ....
   ....
   ....
   ....
   ....
   ....

Quest FINDINGS

Complete the Quest!

Reflect on the engineering and design work you did building your levitating device.

SEP Design Solutions Magnets are used in a variety of industrial and medical applications. How do you think magnet technology might be applied to sports?

....
....
....
....
....

👆 **INTERACTIVITY**

Reflect on Your Levitating Device

Planetary Detective

How can you **build** a device to **detect** magnetic fields on distant planets?

Background

Phenomenon A group of astronomers has approached you for assistance. They are studying three exoplanets, or planets that orbit a star outside our solar system. The three planets orbit in the habitable zone of the star. The astronomers want to know whether or not the planets have magnetic fields, which will help them determine each planet's capacity for supporting life. They are planning to send an exploratory mission to the planets, which will last decades, and they need a lightweight magnetometer. Your first step is to build a test model that will work in the laboratory.

In this investigation, you will build a simple magnetometer, a device that detects magnetic fields, to test models of the three planets. Using evidence from your investigation, you will decide which of the planets have magnetic fields and which one most likely could support life.

Materials

(per group)

- 3 planet models
- 50 mL iron filings
- 2 to 3 paper cups
- pieces of cardboard or small cardboard box
- 60 cm string
- clear tape
- scissors
- 2 to 3 sheets plastic wrap
- 3 to 4 sheets copy paper
- small bar magnet

Safety

Be sure to follow all safety guidelines provided by your teacher. The Safety Appendix of your textbook provides more details about the safety icons.

Earth's magnetic field helps to deflect charged particles in the dangerous solar wind. Without this magnetic field, life would not be possible on our planet.

Design Your Investigation

1. In your investigation, you must build a magnetometer and use it to look for evidence of magnetic fields for models of the three exoplanets, provided by your teacher. Space probes and satellites use this technology to look for evidence of magnetic fields and metals on planets throughout our solar system without coming into contact with the planets.

2. Think about how you can use the available materials to build a magnetometer. Consider the following questions as you work with your group to design your device:

   - How can you use the iron filings to help you detect and observe magnetic forces?

   - How can you use the cups or cardboard along with paper or plastic wrap to design a device that keeps the iron filings contained and allows you to safely observe them?

   - How can you make sure that your device's design allows it to detect magnetic fields without coming into contact with the model?

   - How can you use the magnet to test your device?

3. Sketch your design in the space provided and be sure to label the materials you are using to construct the magnetometer. Then build your device.

4. Plan your investigation by determining how you will use the magnetometer to test the models. Record your plan in the space provided. Consider the following questions as you develop your plan:

   - How can you determine whether or not the planet you are studying has a magnetic field?

   - If you detect magnetic fields, how can you compare the strength of the planets' magnetic forces?

5. After getting your teacher's approval, carry out your investigation. Make a table to record your observations and data in the space provided.

Sketch and Procedure

Data Table and Observations

Analyze and Interpret Data

1. **Apply Concepts** What characteristics do you think a planet needs in order to generate a magnetic field?

....

....

....

....

2. **SEP Use Models** Look at your data and observations for the planet with the strongest magnetic field. The iron filings in your magnetometer were attracted to the magnetic material inside the model. When is the potential energy greater—when the magnetometer is 10 cm from the surface of the planet or when the magnetometer is 3 cm the surface of the planet? Explain.

....

....

....

....

....

3. **CCC Cause and Effect** Your magnetometer did not come into contact with the planet. How do the results of your investigation provide evidence that the magnetic field of the planet interacts with the iron filings in the magnetometer?

....

....

....

....

4. **SEP Construct Arguments** Which of the three planets most likely could support life? Support your response with evidence from your investigation.

....

....

....

....

....

Earth-Sun-Moon System

Investigative Phenomenon

How can models be used to explain the phenomena of lunar phases, eclipses, and seasons?

MS-ESS1-1 Develop and use a model of the Earth-sun-moon system to describe the cyclic patterns of lunar phases, eclipses of the sun and moon, and seasons.

MS-ESS1-2 Develop and use a model to describe the role of gravity in the motions within galaxies and the solar system.

MS-PS2-4 Construct and present arguments using evidence to support the claim that gravitational interactions are attractive and depend on the masses of interacting objects.

What is happening to the sun?

HANDS-ON LAB

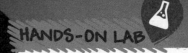

uConnect Model systems showing both Earth and the sun at the center.

What questions do you have about the phenomenon?

....

....

....

....

....

....

....

....

....

....

....

Quest PBL

How are tides related to our place in space?

STEM **Figure It Out** The ebb and flow of the ocean's tides are as steady and sure as the passage of time. Engineers are investigating how to put the power of the tides to work as an alternative to the burning of fossil fuels. In this Quest activity, you will produce a model to help visitors to a tidal power company understand why tidal power is a reliable source of renewable energy. You will explore how and why our position within the solar system causes tides and their patterns. The model that you produce will demonstrate how tides happen.

INTERACTIVITY

It's as Sure as the Tides

MS-ESS1-1

After watching the Quest Kickoff video about tidal energy, think about this source of energy. Complete the diagram by identifying some benefits and drawbacks of tidal energy.

Benefits and Drawbacks of Tidal Energy

Benefits	Drawbacks

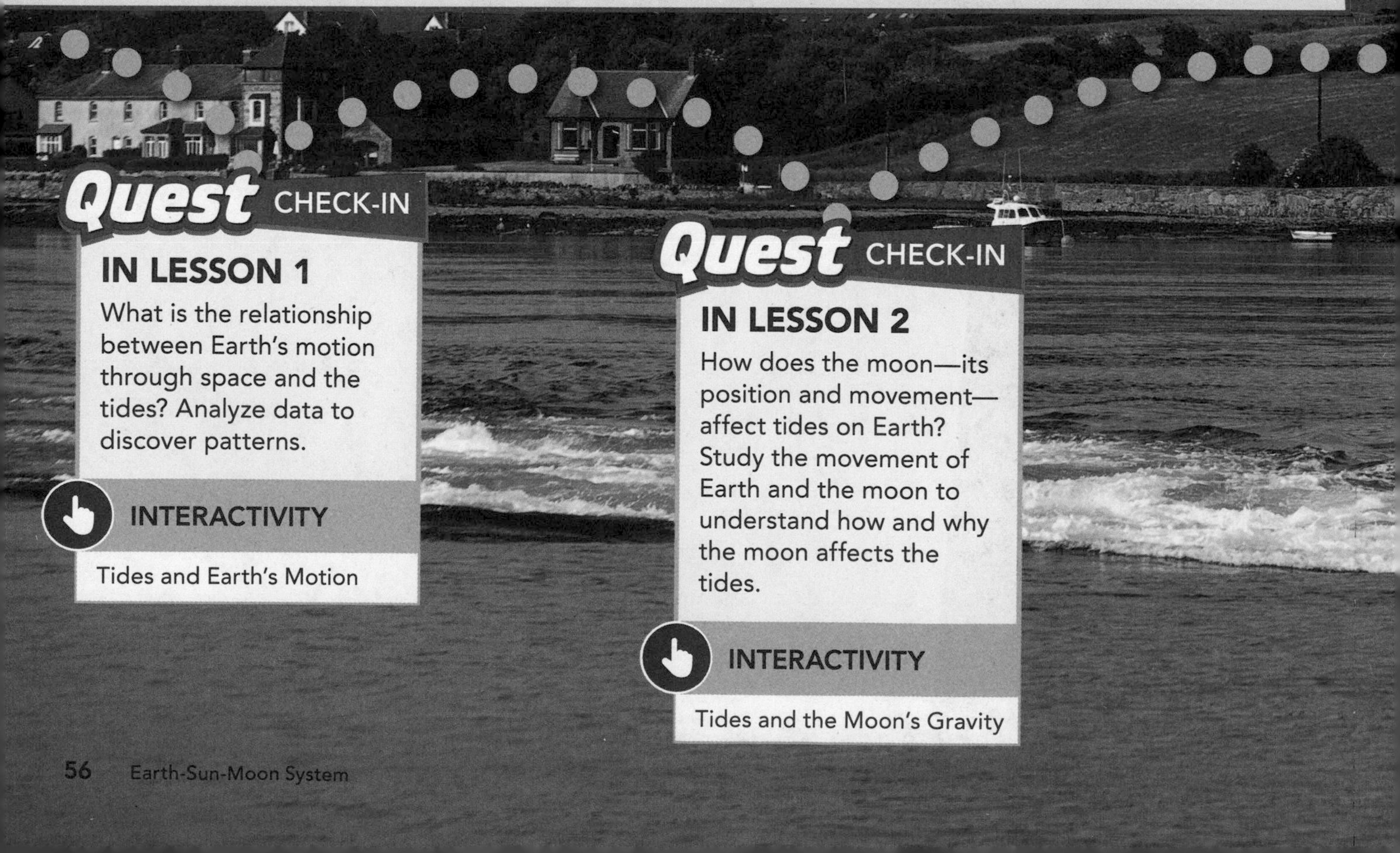

Quest CHECK-IN

IN LESSON 1

What is the relationship between Earth's motion through space and the tides? Analyze data to discover patterns.

INTERACTIVITY

Tides and Earth's Motion

Quest CHECK-IN

IN LESSON 2

How does the moon—its position and movement—affect tides on Earth? Study the movement of Earth and the moon to understand how and why the moon affects the tides.

INTERACTIVITY

Tides and the Moon's Gravity

This tidal turbine in Northern Ireland provides enough electricity to power hundreds of homes.

Quest CHECK-IN

IN LESSON 3

STEM What makes the tides and tidal ranges vary? Investigate how the relative positions of the moon, Earth, and the sun affect the tides.

HANDS-ON LAB

The Moon's Revolution and Tides

Quest FINDINGS

Complete the Quest!

Apply what you've learned to create a model that demonstrates why tides occur and how and why they provide a reliable source of energy.

INTERACTIVITY

Reflect on It's as Sure as the Tides

(1) Movement in Space

HANDS-ON LAB

✓Investigate Model how stars' positions change relative to a night sky observer on Earth.

MS-ESS1-1 Develop and use a model of the Earth-sun-moon system to describe the cyclic patterns of lunar phases, eclipses of the sun and moon, and seasons.

Connect It !

🖊 **Circle the objects that appear to be moving in this photo.**

SEP Apply Scientific Reasoning How can you tell that an object in space is moving through the sky?

....

....

The Night Sky

Why do the stars appear to move? What makes the moon shine through the darkness? Aryabhata I (ar yah BAH tah) was an early astronomer who thought about these questions. He was born in 476 CE in what is now India. Aryabhata I wrote that the moon and the planets shine because they reflect light from the sun. He came up with these conclusions based solely on his **observations** of the sky with his naked eye.

Stars, Planets, and the Moon You may look up on a clear night, such as the one shown in **Figure 1**, and see stars, the moon, planets, meteors, and comets, much as Aryabhata I did. Earth's moon is the brightest and largest object in our night sky. The moon is Earth's only natural satellite. A **satellite** is a body that orbits a planet. By contrast, stars appear as tiny points of light. However, a **star** is a giant ball of superheated gas, or plasma, composed of hydrogen and helium. As seen from Earth, the positions of stars relative to each other do not seem to change.

Have you ever noticed objects that change position from night to night against the background of the stars? These are planets. A **planet** is an object that orbits the sun, is large enough to have become rounded by its own gravity, and has cleared the area of its orbit of any debris. There are eight planets in our solar system.

INTERACTIVITY

Answer a poll about things you have seen in the night sky.

Academic Vocabulary
How does making observations help scientists come up with new ideas?

....

....

....

....

....

Objects in the Sky
Figure 1 On a clear night, you can often see objects in space in the night sky.

HANDS-ON LAB

⟲**Investigate** Model how stars' positions change relative to a night sky observer on Earth.

Meteors and Comets Have you ever seen a shooting star? These sudden bright streaks are called meteors. A **meteor** is a streak of light produced when a small piece of rock or ice, known as a meteoroid, burns up as it enters Earth's atmosphere. You can see a meteor on almost any clear night.

Comets are rarer sights than meteors. A **comet** is a cold mixture of dust and ice that develops a long trail of light as it approaches the sun. When a comet is far from the sun, it is frozen. As it gets close to the sun, the cloud trailing behind the comet forms a glowing tail made up of hot dust and gases.

Perhaps the most famous comet is Halley's Comet. This highly visible comet was documented by Edmund Halley, who calculated its orbit and predicted its next appearance in the sky. Sure enough, the comet appeared as he predicted in 1758, although Halley didn't live to see it. It has continued to appear about every 75 years, last appearing in 1986.

Math Toolbox

Halley's Comet

In 1910, Halley's Comet traveled close to Earth—about 1/7 of the distance from Earth to the sun. Earth's distance from the sun is 149.6 million kilometers.

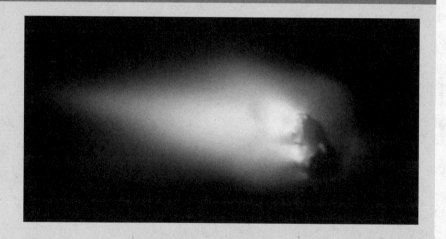

1. **Create an Equation** How close was Halley's Comet to Earth in 1910? Create an equation to answer the question.

....

2. **SEP Interpret Data** Estimate the next three years when Halley's Comet will appear.

....

....

3. **CCC Scale, Proportion, and Quantity** The core of Halley's comet is oblong in shape, with its longest dimension 16 km long. Earth's diameter is about 12,700 km. What is the ratio of Earth's diameter to Halley's comet's longest dimension?

....

Finding Constellations

Figure 2 ✏️ Star charts can help you to find constellations in the night sky. This is a summer chart for the Northern Hemisphere. Find these constellations in the star chart. Then write each constellation's name by its picture.

Northern Horizon

Eastern Horizon

Western Horizon

Southern Horizon

Constellations

For thousands of years, human beings in many cultures have seen patterns in groups of stars and given them names. A pattern or group of stars that people imagine represents a figure, animal, or object is a **constellation**. Often, as in the ancient Roman and Greek cultures, constellations supported specific mythologies. Today, scientists divide the sky into 88 constellations. Some constellations are named for people or animals from Greek myths. Pegasus and Perseus, for example, are both mythological characters and constellations. Study the constellations shown in **Figure 2**.

✅ **CHECK POINT** **Integrate with Visuals** How do the pictures in **Figure 2** help you remember the constellations?

....

....

....

....

📓 **Reflect** In your science notebook, write about the patterns of stars you see in the night sky.

61

Star Trails

Figure 3 This time-lapse photo taken from the White Mountains near Bishop, California captures the movements of stars. The North Star happens to be aligned with the axis of Earth, directly "above" the North Pole.

Claim ✎ Circle the North Star in the photo.

Evidence What makes you think the star you circled is the North Star?

....
....
....

Reasoning Explain your reasoning.

....
....
....
....
....
....
....

Movement in the Sky

Stars, planets, and other objects appear to move over time. They do move in space, but those actual motions and their apparent, or visible, motions may be very different. The positions of objects in the sky depend on the motions of Earth.

Stars generally appear to move from east to west through the night. Toward the poles, stars appear to take a circular path, as shown in **Figure 3**. As Aryabhata I thought, this apparent motion is caused by Earth rotating toward the east. The sun's apparent motion is also caused by Earth's rotation.

Seasonal Changes Constellations and star patterns remain the same from year to year, but the constellations visible to you vary from season to season. For example, you can find the constellation Orion in the eastern sky on winter evenings. But by spring, you'll see Orion in the west, disappearing below the horizon shortly after sunset.

These seasonal changes are caused by Earth's revolution, or orbit, around the sun. Each night, the position of most stars shifts slightly to the west. After a while, you no longer see stars once visible in the west, and previously unseen stars appear in the east. After six months, Earth is on the other side of the sun. Constellations that used to appear in the night sky are now behind the sun, where the sun's bright light blocks them from our vision during the day.

Planets Planets appear to move against the background of stars. In fact, the word *planet* comes from a Greek word meaning "wanderer." Because the planets all orbit the sun in about the same plane, or level, they appear to move through a narrow band in the sky. This band is called the zodiac.

Some planets are visible all night long. Mars, Jupiter, and Saturn are all farther from the sun than Earth is. When Earth passes between them and the sun, these three planets are visible after sunset, once the sun's bright light no longer blocks the view. You can see Venus and Mercury only in the evening or morning. They are closer to the sun than Earth, and so they always appear close to the sun, as shown in **Figure 4**.

☑ CHECK POINT **Cite Textual Evidence** Why would you need two different star charts for finding constellations in the summer and the winter?

....

....

....

....

....

Mercury and Venus
Figure 4 The planets Mercury and Venus never appear far from the sun in the sky.

SEP Use Models ✎ Where in this image is Venus farthest from the sun? Place a dot on the image to indicate the spot.

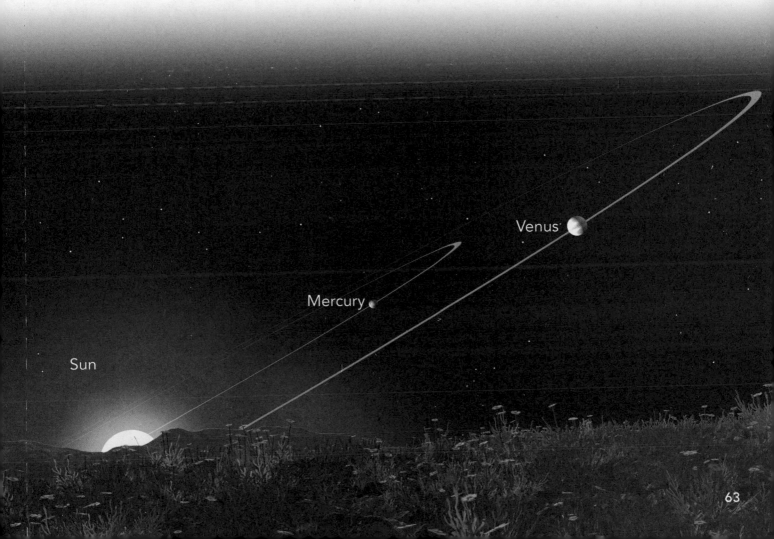

Venus

Mercury

Sun

63

Models of the Solar System

From here on Earth, it seems as if our planet is stationary and that the sun, moon, and stars are moving around Earth. Ancient peoples such as the Greeks, Chinese, and Mayans noticed that although the stars seemed to move, they stayed in the same position relative to one another.

Geocentric Model Many early observers, including the Greek philosopher, Aristotle, thought Earth was the center of the universe, with all the planets and stars circling it, as shown in **Figure 5**. Because *ge* is the Greek word for "Earth," an Earth-centered model is known as a **geocentric** (jee oh SEN trik) model.

In about 140 C.E., the Greek astronomer Ptolemy further developed Aristotle's geocentric model. In Ptolemy's model, the planets made small circles called epicycles as they moved along their orbital paths. This model seemed to explain the motions observed in the sky. As a result, Ptolemy's geocentric model was widely accepted for nearly 1,500 years after his death.

Literacy Connection

Integrate with Visuals
As you look at **Figure 5**, think about why this diagram was included on this page. Highlight the portion of the text that relates to the diagram. How does this diagram add to the information you gained by reading the text?

....

....

....

....

....

....

....

The Geocentric Model
Figure 5 This geocentric model shows our solar system, with Earth in the center. The other planets orbit Earth and move along their epicycles at the same time.

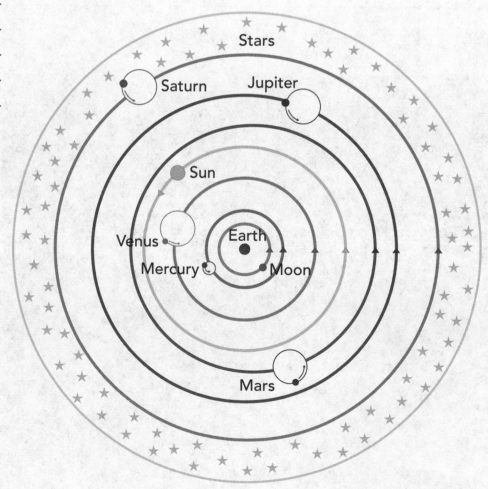

Heliocentric Model Not everybody believed in the geocentric system. An ancient Greek scientist named Aristarchus, who lived over 400 years before Ptolemy, developed a sun-centered or **heliocentric** (hee lee oh SEN trik) model. *Helios* is Greek for "sun." In a heliocentric system, Earth and the other planets revolve around the sun. This model was not well received. Many people insisted that Earth had to be at the center of the universe.

Figure 6 lists four scientists who worked to expand and prove the heliocentric model of the solar system. The Polish astronomer Nicolaus Copernicus further developed the heliocentric model. Copernicus proposed that Earth's rotation and revolution around the sun explained the observed movements of the stars and planets. He published his work in 1543. Copernicus's theory would eventually revolutionize the science of astronomy, the study of space.

Early heliocentric models assumed that planets moved in perfect circles. Their models fit existing observations fairly well. But in the late 1500s, the Danish astronomer Tycho Brahe (TEE koh BRAH huh) made much more accurate observations. Brahe's assistant, Johannes Kepler, used the observations to figure out the shape of the planets' orbits. When he used circular orbits, his calculations did not fit the observations. After years of detailed calculations, Kepler found that the orbit of each planet is actually an **ellipse**, an oval shape, rather than a perfect circle.

Galileo's Discovery For many years, people continued to believe the geocentric model. However, evidence collected by the Italian scientist Galileo Galilei gradually convinced others that the heliocentric model was correct. In 1610, Galileo, using a telescope that he constructed himself, discovered moons orbiting Jupiter. These Galilean moons showed that not everything in the sky travels around Earth.

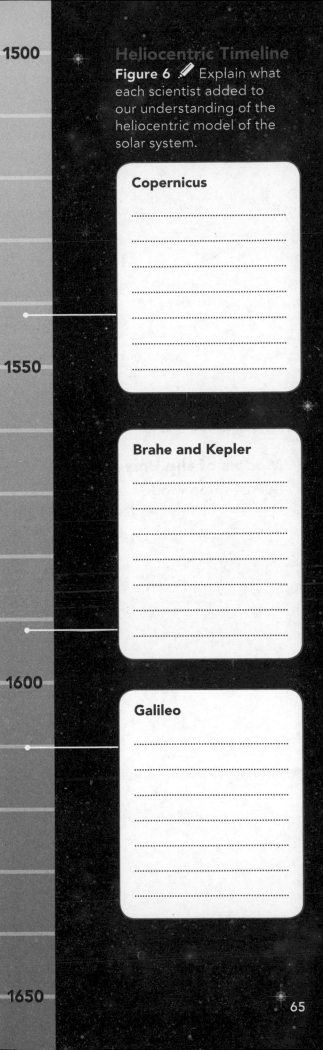

Heliocentric Timeline

Figure 6 ✏ Explain what each scientist added to our understanding of the heliocentric model of the solar system.

1500

1550

1600

1650

Copernicus

Brahe and Kepler

Galileo

INTERACTIVITY

Determine how seasonal changes in our perception of stars support a specific model of the solar system.

Confirming the Heliocentric Model Galileo also made other observations that supported Copernicus's theory that the sun was the center of the solar system. For example, Galileo discovered that Venus goes through phases similar to the moon's phases. But Venus would not have a full set of phases if both it and the sun circled around Earth. Therefore, Galileo reasoned, the geocentric model did not hold true.

CHECK POINT **Cite Textual Evidence** How does the development of the heliocentric model show how scientific ideas change over time?

....

....

....

....

....

Model It

Models of the Universe

SEP Develop Models Draw Galileo's heliocentric system. Show and label the evidence he produced to support his model.

1. Predict Two photographers take time-lapse photos of the night sky. One of them is at the equator. The other is at the South Pole. Which photo will show stars that never rise or set? Explain.

....

....

....

....

....

2. CCC System Models Describe two models that show how Earth and the sun move in space relative to each other.

....

....

....

....

....

....

....

3. Infer What observations made by Galileo supported Copernicus's theory about the solar system?

....

....

....

....

....

....

....

4. SEP Construct Explanations Which patterns in space are predictable? Why?

....

....

....

5. CCC Cause and Effect What causes the stars to appear to move across the night sky?

....

....

....

 **CHECK-IN**

In this lesson, you learned why the stars in the night sky seem to move. You learned that various objects move, or seem to move, in space. You also discovered how Earth and the other planets move in relation to the sun.

Evaluate If the relative positions of the sun and moon affect the ocean's tides, why would it be smart for sailors and other people who work on the ocean to understand patterns in the Earth-sun-moon system?

....

....

....

....

👆 **INTERACTIVITY**

Tides and Earth's Motion

Go online to analyze images and data about tides and look for connections in the patterns you see.

Earth's Movement in Space

HANDS-ON LAB

∪Investigate Review the differences between mass and weight and how weight is affected by gravity.

MS-ESS1-1 Develop and use a model of the Earth-sun-moon system to describe the cyclic patterns of lunar phases, eclipses of the sun and moon, and seasons.

MS-ESS1-2 Develop and use a model to describe the role of gravity in the motions within galaxies and the solar system.

MS-PS2-4 Construct and present arguments using evidence to support the claim that gravitational interactions are attractive and depend on the masses of interacting objects.

Connect It !

✏ **Draw an arrrow on the image to indicate which direction you would find the sun relative to Earth.**

SEP Apply Scientific Reasoning Which part of Earth is experiencing daytime in the image?

....

....

....

How Earth Moves

The apparent motion of the sun, moon, and stars in the sky is a result of the way Earth itself moves through space. Earth, as well as the other planets, moves around the sun in two separate ways: rotation and revolution.

Rotation To help describe Earth's movement, scientists have named an imaginary line that passes from the North Pole, through the Earth's center, to the South Pole. This line is known as Earth's **axis**, and the spinning of Earth on its axis is called **rotation**.

Look at **Figure 1**. You can see that half of Earth is lit and half is in darkness. Earth rotates from west to east (see **Figure 2**.) As it rotates, objects in the sky appear to move in the direction opposite of Earth's rotation.

As Earth rotates eastward, the sun appears to move west across the sky. As Earth continues to turn to the east, the sun appears to set in the west. Because sunlight can't reach the side of Earth facing away from the sun, it is night there. It takes Earth about 24 hours to rotate once. As you know, each of these 24-hour cycles is called a day.

INTERACTIVITY

Investigate the patterns in Earth's rotation and revolution.

Day and Night

Figure 1 Day occurs on the part of Earth that is turned toward the sun. Night occurs on the part of Earth that is turned away from the sun.

Earth's Axis

Figure 2 ✏️ Earth spins on its axis, rotating from west to east to cause day and night. Shade the part of Earth that is experiencing night.

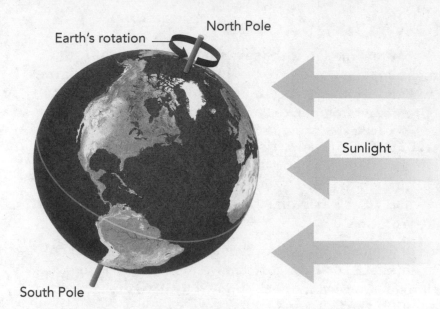

North Pole

Earth's rotation

Sunlight

South Pole

Revolution
As you read this page, do you feel as if you are moving? You may not feel it, but as Earth rotates, it is traveling around the sun. **Revolution** is the movement of one object around another. One revolution of Earth around the sun takes one year. Like other planets, Earth's path, or **orbit**, around the sun is an ellipse, an oval shape. The ellipse brings the planet closest to the sun in January.

SEP Develop Models ✏️ How could you model Earth's movements? Design a model using real objects to represent Earth and the sun. Explain how you could use these objects to illustrate Earth's motions. Include both Earth's rotation and revolution in your design and explanation.

....

....

....

....

The Seasons

The extent of seasonal change in any given place on Earth depends on several factors, including how far away that place is from the equator. In many cases, the farther away a place is from the equator, the more widely its seasonal temperatures can vary. This is because of how sunlight hits Earth.

When we look at areas near the equator, we see that sunlight hits Earth's surface very directly. This sunlight is concentrated in the smallest possible area. Near the North and South Poles, sunlight hitting Earth forms a large angle with the local vertical, so the same amount of sunlight spreads over a greater area. That's why it is warmer near the equator than near the poles.

Seasonal differences in temperature are dependent on the tilt of Earth's axis. If the axis were straight up and down relative to Earth's orbit, temperatures in a given area would remain constant year-round, and there would be no seasons. However, Earth's axis is tilted at an angle of 23.5° from the vertical. Therefore, as Earth revolves around the sun, the north end of its axis is tilted away from the sun for part of the year and toward the sun for part of the year. Earth has seasons because its axis is tilted as it revolves around the sun. The direction of the Earth's tilt is fixed. It does not change as it revolves around the sun.

Figure 3 shows how Earth moves during the year. In June, the Northern Hemisphere is tilted toward the sun and experiences summer. The sun's rays fall on a relatively small area and the temperatures are warmer. In December, the Northern Hemisphere is tilted away from the sun and experiences winter. The sun's rays fall on a relatively large area, so temperatures are lower. During March and September, sunlight strikes both hemispheres equally, causing the mild temperatures felt in spring and autumn.

Literacy Connection

Cite Textual Evidence
Reread the second and third paragraphs. Underline the evidence that supports the statement that seasons are caused by the tilt of Earth's axis.

Seasons

Figure 3 Earth's tilted axis affects the strength of sunlight in different places throughout the year. Look at the diagram. Which month is showing the South Pole in compelete darkness?

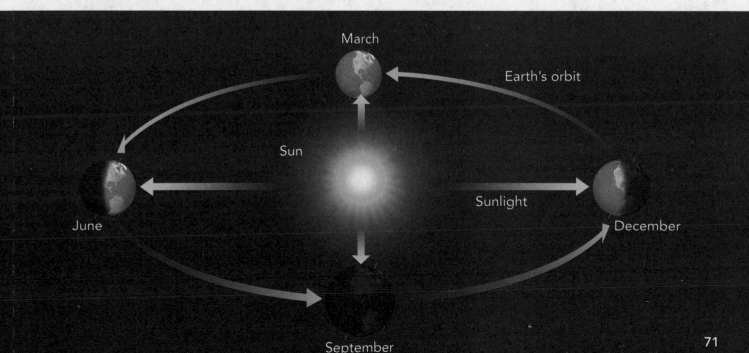

March

Earth's orbit

Sun

Sunlight

June

December

September

INTERACTIVITY

Explore how Earth's tilted axis and revolution influence the seasons.

Day Length

The tilt of Earth's axis also affects day length. The hemisphere that is tilted toward the sun has more hours of day than night. Points on Earth near the poles have the most drastic changes in day length. In Kiruna, Sweden, shown in **Figure 4**, the sun remains below the horizon throughout the day for most of January. However, in June the sun never fully sets.

Solstices and Equinoxes

In each hemisphere, there is one day per year when the sun appears highest in the sky. Each of these days is called a **solstice**. Solstices occur when either the Northern or Southern Hemisphere is at its strongest tilt towards the sun.

Halfway between the solstices, neither hemisphere is tilted toward the sun. Each of these days is called an **equinox**, which means "equal night." This day occurs when the sun passes directly overhead at the equator at noon, and night and day are both 12 hours long.

The solstices and equinoxes occur at opposite times in the Northern and Southern Hemispheres. In the Northern Hemisphere, the summer solstice occurs around June 21, and the winter solstice occurs around December 22. However, in the Southern Hemisphere, these dates are opposite of what they are in the Northern Hemisphere. Equinoxes occur in both the Northern and Southern Hemispheres around September 22 and March 21.

Short Days

Figure 4 At noon in January, the sun is still low in the sky in Sweden.

Gravity and Orbits

The force that keeps Earth in orbit around the sun and the moon in orbit around Earth is the same force that prevents you from flying away when you jump. That force is gravity.

Gravity In the 1600s, an English scientist named Isaac Newton was curious about why the moon orbits Earth. In his work *Principia*, Newton contended that there must be a force, or a push and pull, acting between Earth and the moon.

Newton **hypothesized** that the same force that pulls the moon toward Earth also pulls apples to the ground when they fall from a tree. This force that attracts all objects toward each other is called **gravity**. Newton's **law of universal gravitation** states that every object in the universe attracts every other object. The strength of the force of gravity between two objects depends on two factors: the masses of the objects and the distance between them. Mass is the amount of matter in an object. Because Earth is so massive, it exerts a much greater force on you than your textbook exerts on you.

The measure of the force of gravity on an object is called weight. Mass doesn't change, but an object's weight can change depending on its location. On the moon, you would weigh about one-sixth as much as on Earth. The moon has less mass than Earth, so the pull of the moon's gravity on you would also be less. In space, as shown in **Figure 5**, you have no weight at all.

Gravity is also affected by the distance between two objects. The force of gravity decreases as distance increases. If the distance between two objects doubles, the force of gravity decreases to one-fourth of its original value.

HANDS-ON LAB

ıı**Investigate** Review the differences between mass and weight and how weight is affected by gravity.

Academic Vocabulary

How have you heard the term *hypothesize* used before?

....

....

....

....

73

Inertia If the sun and Earth are constantly pulling on one another because of gravity, why doesn't Earth fall into the sun? The fact that such a collision has not occurred shows that a factor called inertia is at work.

Inertia is the tendency of an object to resist a change in motion. You feel the effects of inertia when you are riding in a car and it stops suddenly, but you keep moving forward. The more mass an object has, the greater its inertia. An object with greater inertia is more difficult to start or stop.

Isaac Newton stated his ideas about inertia as a scientific law. Newton's first law of motion says that an object at rest will stay at rest and an object in motion will stay in motion with a constant speed and direction, unless acted on by a force.

Math Toolbox
Gravity vs. Distance

Imagine that a spacecraft is leaving Earth's surface. How does the force of gravity between the rocket and the planet change?

Distance from Earth's Center (planet's radius = 1)	1	2	3	4
Force of Gravity on the Spacecraft (million newtons)	4	1	0.44	0.25

1. **SEP Construct Graphs** 🖉 Create a line graph of the data above.

2. **Analyze Quantitative Relationships** What is the force of gravity on the spacecraft at twice the planet's radius from its center?

   ....

3. **Make Predictions** What would the force of gravity on the spacecraft be at a distance of 8 radii?

   ....

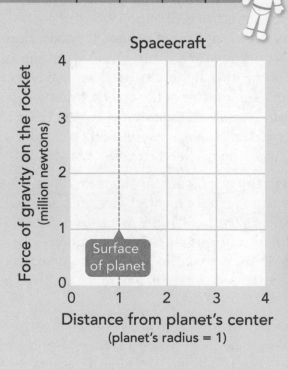

Spacecraft

Force of gravity on the rocket (million newtons)

Surface of planet

Distance from planet's center (planet's radius = 1)

Orbital Motion So, the moon travels through space at the same speed because of its inertia. But, it is constantly changing direction to remain in orbit around Earth. Newton concluded that inertia and gravity combine to keep the moon in orbit around Earth. You can see how this occurs in **Figure 6**.

Without Earth's gravity, the moon would veer away from Earth in a straight line. Earth's gravity pulls the moon inward and prevents it from moving away in a straight line. The combination of these two factors results in a curved orbital path. Similarly, planets are held in their elliptical orbits around the sun by the combined forces of gravity and inertia.

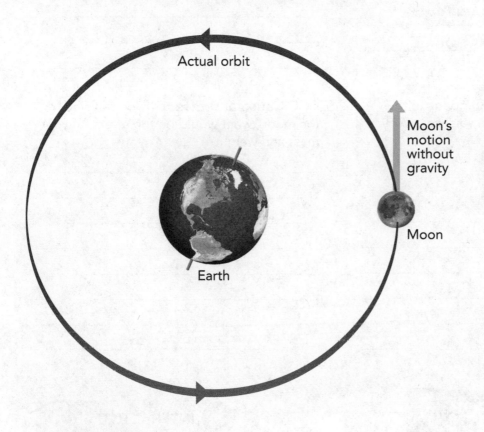

Actual orbit

Moon's motion without gravity

Moon

Earth

Orbital Motion

Figure 6 ✏ Gravity and inertia keep the moon in orbit around Earth. Complete the diagram by drawing an arrow to indicate the force of gravity Earth exerts on the moon as it orbits Earth.

☑ CHECK POINT **Cite Textual Evidence** What factors affect the strength of the pull of gravity between two objects?

....

....

....

....

....

....

....

....

☑ LESSON 2 Check

MS-ESS1-1, MS-ESS1-2, MS-PS2-4

1. Identify What are the two ways Earth moves?

....

....

2. CCC Patterns What causes the pattern of day and night? What causes the pattern of the seasons?

....

....

....

3. Draw Conclusions What happens to the length of the day during the solstices? Why does this occur?

....

....

....

....

....

....

....

4. SEP Construct Explanations What parts of Earth generally have the highest temperatures? Which have the lowest? What causes this difference?

....

....

....

....

....

....

5. CCC Cause and Effect If you traveled to the moon, what would be the effect on your mass and weight?

....

....

....

....

....

....

CHECK-IN

In this lesson, you learned about the way that the sun interacts with Earth to produce day, night, and the seasons. You also discovered how gravity, mass, and inertia affect the movement of Earth and the moon.

Infer When the sun, moon, and Earth are aligned, ocean tides are larger—high tide is higher, low tide is lower—than when they are not aligned. How might this relate to gravity?

....

....

....

....

👆 INTERACTIVITY

Tides and the Moon's Gravity

Go online to study models of the motions of Earth and the moon and observe how these motions affect the tides on Earth's surface.

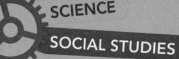

Tracking
Time in the Sky

Will your birthday fall on a weekend this year? Better check the calendar! A calendar organizes time into days, months, and years. It may seem like a simple grid of squares, but a calendar is actually a measurement of time based on patterns of movement among Earth, the sun, and the moon.

Egyptian Calendar (3rd Millenium BCE)
The ancient Egyptians created one of the first calendars. They figured out that a year—the time it takes for Earth to orbit the sun—was 365 days long. They used the repeating phases of the moon to divide a year into 12 months of 30 days each and tacked on five extra days at the end of the year.

Julian Calendar (46 BCE)
The Romans borrowed the Egyptian calendar, but they noticed that it didn't always line up with the first day of spring. It actually takes 365 ¼ days for Earth to orbit the sun. So, Julius Caesar added an extra day every four years to keep the calendar on track. This extra day is inserted into a "leap year," so that February has 29 days instead of 28.

Gregorian Calendar (1582 CE)
After a few centuries, it became clear that the Roman calendar also wasn't quite right. In fact, it was almost 11 minutes off each year. That may not sound like much, but by the year 1582, the first day of spring was a full ten days too early. To fix the problem, Pope Gregory XIII reset and tweaked the calendar, giving us the one we still use today.

CONNECT TO YOU

Divide this year by 4. If the year is evenly divisible by 4, it's a leap year. Years that end in 00 are exceptions. They must be divisible by 400!

The ancient Egyptians created a calendar to keep track of civic events such as festivals. Archeologists discovered this calendar in the Temple of Karnak in Luxor.

③ Phases and Eclipses

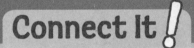**Investigate** Research to find out why we don't see the dark side of the moon from Earth.

MS-ESS1-1 Develop and use a model of the Earth-sun-moon system to describe the cyclic patterns of lunar phases, eclipses of the sun and moon, and seasons.

Connect It !

✐ **Observe the image of the moon in Figure 1. Draw several other shapes that you have seen the moon take.**

SEP Construct Explanations What might be causing these changes?

....

....

....

CCC Cause and Effect How is Earth affected by the moon?

....

....

The Appearance of the Moon

When the moon is full, it shines so brightly that it makes the night sky significantly brighter. At these times, when viewed from Earth, the moon is round or almost round. Other times, the moon is just a thin crescent in the sky, seeming to emit a small strand of light, as in **Figure 1**. The different shapes of the moon you see are called **phases**. Phases are caused by the motions of the moon around Earth.

The Two Sides of the Moon When you look at the moon when it's full, you may see what looks like a face. You are actually seeing some of the most dramatic features of the moon, a pattern of light-colored and dark-colored areas on the moon's surface. The dark-colored areas are low, flat plains of lava called *maria*. You may also be able to detect brighter patterns that indicate highland areas, often dotted with craters.

For observers from Earth these distinctive patterns on the moon never move. The side of the moon that always faces Earth is called the near side. The side of the moon that always faces away from Earth is the far side, or dark side. To find out why the same side of the moon always faces Earth, you must study the motion of the moon around Earth.

INTERACTIVITY

Investigate why the moon is sometimes visible during the day.

Reflect Look up at the sky tonight. What phase of the moon do you see? In your science notebook, track the phases of the moon. Based on your observations, what is the position of the moon in relation to the sun and Earth?

Moon Phases

Figure 1 This crescent moon over Los Angeles, California is visible over the horizon shortly after sunset.

Lunar Motion

Figure 2 🖊 This diagram shows the rotation and revolution of the moon. Write the letter M next to the two remaining images of the moon to show how the moon is facing Earth at each phase. How would the moon appear from Earth if the moon did not rotate?

....

....

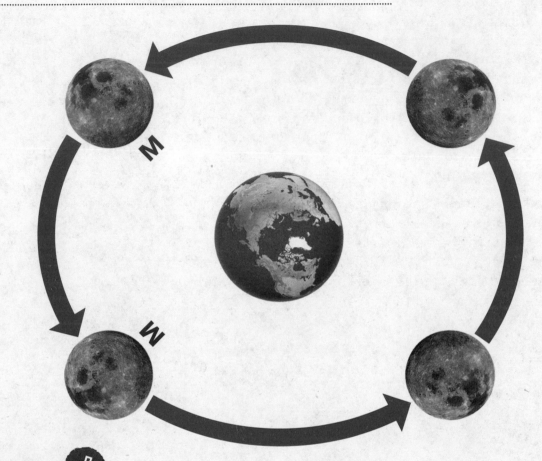

Motions of the Moon The moon, like Earth, rotates and revolves. The moon revolves around Earth and also rotates on its own axis. The moon rotates once on its axis in the same time that it takes to revolve once around Earth, as shown in **Figure 2**. Thus, a "day" on the moon is the same length as a "year" on the moon. This also explains why you always see the same side of the moon from Earth.

If you could look at the moon from space, you would see that half of the moon is always lit by the sun. The amount of the moon's surface that is lit is constant. But because the moon orbits Earth, the part of the lit surface that is visible from Earth changes. The phase of the moon you see depends on how much of the sunlit side of the moon faces Earth. These periods of light and darkness occur in predictable patterns, as shown in **Figure 3**.

Phases of the Moon During the new moon phase, the moon is between Earth and the sun. The side of the moon facing Earth is dark and the opposite side of the moon is facing the sun. As the moon revolves around Earth, the side of the moon you see gradually becomes more illuminated by direct sunlight.

After about a week, the angle formed by the sun, moon, and Earth is about 90 degrees. This is called the first quarter moon and it is half lit and half dark. About halfway through the moon's revolution, you see the full sunlit side of the moon, called a full moon. About a week later, the sun is shining on the other half of the moon, creating a third quarter moon. At this time you see half of the lit side. After about 29.5 days, the pattern begins again and a new moon occurs.

☑ **CHECK POINT** **Translate Information** Use **Figure 3** to describe what is happening during a waning crescent.

....

....

....

....

👆 **INTERACTIVITY**

Explore why the moon sometimes appears as a crescent in the sky.

▶ **VIDEO**

Find out more about the changing appearance of the moon as we see it from Earth.

Moon Phases
Figure 3 ✏ In the empty circle, draw what a waning crescent moon looks like from Earth.

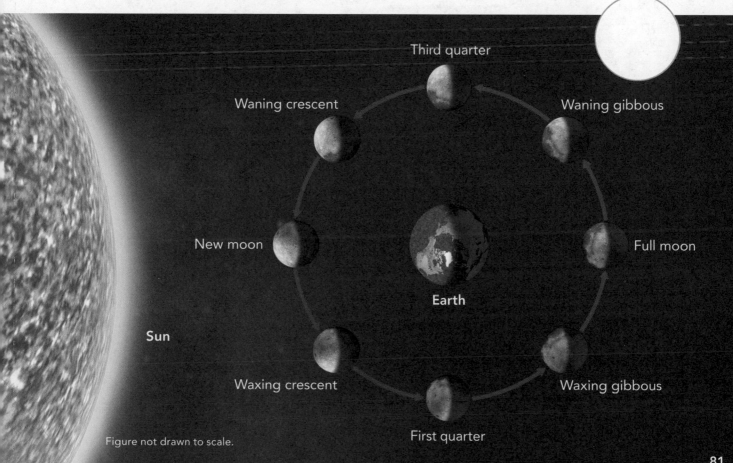

Third quarter

Waning crescent

Waning gibbous

New moon

Full moon

Earth

Waxing crescent

Waxing gibbous

Sun

First quarter

Figure not drawn to scale.

81

INTERACTIVITY

Learn more about the phases of the moon and eclipses.

VIDEO

Discover what it's like to work in a planetarium.

Eclipses

When an object in space comes between the sun and a third object, it casts a shadow on the third object, causing an **eclipse**. There are two types of eclipses, solar eclipses and lunar eclipses, as shown in **Figure 4**.

Every month there is a new moon and a full moon, but eclipses don't occur every month. The plane of the moon's orbit around Earth is off by about 5 degrees from the plane of Earth's orbit around the sun. During most months, the shadow cast by Earth or the moon misses the other object.

During an eclipse, the very darkest part of the shadow where the light from the sun is completely blocked is the **umbra**. Only people within the umbra experience a total solar eclipse. The moon's umbra is fairly narrow, while Earth's is much broader. Because a lunar eclipse is visible from every point on Earth's night side, more people have a view of a total lunar eclipse than of a total solar eclipse.

The area of the shadow where the sun is only partially blocked is called the **penumbra**. During a solar eclipse, people in the penumbra see only a partial eclipse. A partial lunar eclipse occurs when the moon passes partly into the umbra of Earth's shadow. The edge of the umbra appears blurry, and you can watch it pass across the moon for two or three hours.

✓ CHECK POINT **Determine Central Ideas** Why isn't there an eclipse every month?

....

....

....

Two Types of Eclipses

Figure 4 ✏️ Draw an *X* on each diagram to show a spot where each eclipse can be seen. Add labels for the Earth's penumbra and umbra in the lunar eclipse diagram. Mark a *P* to show the places a moon could be during a partial lunar eclipse.

👆 **INTERACTIVITY**

Use a virtual activity to learn more about eclipses.

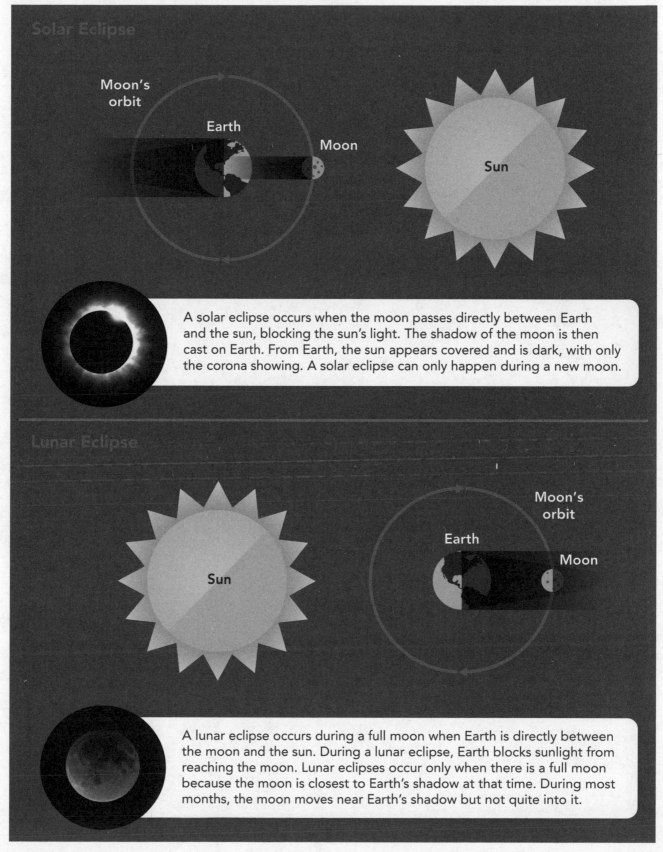

Solar Eclipse

Moon's orbit

Earth

Moon

Sun

A solar eclipse occurs when the moon passes directly between Earth and the sun, blocking the sun's light. The shadow of the moon is then cast on Earth. From Earth, the sun appears covered and is dark, with only the corona showing. A solar eclipse can only happen during a new moon.

Lunar Eclipse

Sun

Moon's orbit

Earth

Moon

A lunar eclipse occurs during a full moon when Earth is directly between the moon and the sun. During a lunar eclipse, Earth blocks sunlight from reaching the moon. Lunar eclipses occur only when there is a full moon because the moon is closest to Earth's shadow at that time. During most months, the moon moves near Earth's shadow but not quite into it.

Model It

Solar and Lunar Eclipses

Solar and lunar eclipses occur when the sun, moon, and Earth are perfectly aligned.

SEP Develop Models How could you represent Earth, the moon, and the sun during an eclipse? Use real objects to create a model of a solar eclipse and a lunar eclipse. Think about what you could use as a light source to represent the sun. What positions would your objects need to be in to illustrate each type of eclipse? Draw and label the plan for your models.

☑ LESSON 3 Check

1. CCC Patterns Why does the moon have phases?

....

....

....

....

....

....

....

2. SEP Explain Phenomena In what positions are the sun, moon, and Earth during a full moon?

....

....

....

....

3. CCC Cause and Effect What causes a total lunar eclipse?

....

....

....

....

....

4. SEP Construct Explanations Under what circumstances might you be able to view a partial solar eclipse instead of a full solar eclipse?

....

....

....

....

....

Quest CHECK-IN

In this lesson, you learned about how Earth, the moon, and the sun interact to create the phases of the moon, eclipses, and tides.

SEP Evaluate Information What does the pattern among the moon's phases and the cycle of tides suggest about how reliable tidal power would be?

....

....

....

....

....

....

HANDS-ON LAB

The Moon's Revolution and Tides

Go online for a downloadable worksheet of this lab. Investigate how the position of the moon relative to Earth and the sun affects tides and to explore why some tidal ranges vary over time.

◔ MS-ESS1-1

Evidence-Based Assessment

Gita is constructing a model to help her younger sister in science class. She hopes to use the model to demonstrate how the sun, Earth, and the moon interact so that her sister can describe and explain patterns in the cycles of this system. Gita wants her sister to be able to describe the following phenomena using the model:

• the phases of the moon

• the seasons on Earth

• solar and lunar eclipses

Gita's model is shown here. Gita labels E1, E2, E3, and E4 to show four positions of Earth in its orbit around the sun. She labels M1, M2, M3, and M4 to show four positions of the moon in its orbit around Earth.

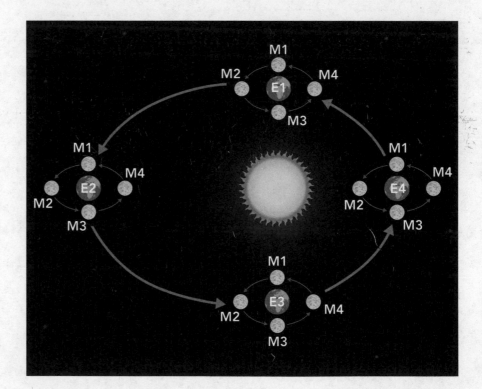

1. **CCC System Models** If Earth is at position E1 on the model and there is a new moon, then what is the moon's position?
   A. M1
   B. M2
   C. M3
   D. M4

2. **CCC Patterns** Complete the table to identify the positions of Earth and the moon in their respective orbits for each phenomenon listed.

Phenomenon	Earth's Position	Moon's Position
lunar eclipse		M4
solar eclipse	E3	
full moon	E1	

3. **SEP Use Models** Which of the following pieces of information cannot be described using Gita's model? Check all that apply.
   ☐ The patterns of the seasons on Earth.
   ☐ The phases of the moon.
   ☐ The tilt of Earth on its axis.
   ☐ The position of Earth at the solstices.
   ☐ The position of Earth at the equinoxes.

4. **SEP Construct Explanations** Explain how Gita's sister can also use the model to show how patterns in the interactions among the sun, Earth, and the moon allow us to predict when lunar phases and eclipses occur.

....
....
....
....
....
....
....
....
....
....
....
....

Quest FINDINGS

Complete the Quest!

Think about ways to develop your model to demonstrate how the tides occur.

CCC Identify Limitations What are some of the limitations of your model for the visitor center? How could you make your model more accurate?

....
....
....
....

👆 **INTERACTIVITY**

Reflect on It's as Sure as the Tides

MS-ESS1-1

Modeling Lunar Phases

Can you **design a model** to describe how the **moon's motion** is related to its **phases?**

Background

Phenomenon One of the greatest achievements of our ancestors was learning to make sense of the repeating patterns in the phases of the moon. People began organizing time and planning major events, such as planting and harvesting crops, according to these cycles, resulting in the earliest stages of human civilization.

In this investigation, you will design a model, using available materials, to show the relationship between the moon's motion around Earth and the moon's phases.

Materials

(per group)

- bright flashlight
- one small foam ball
- one large foam ball
- sharpened pencils or skewers

New Moon   First Quarter   Full Moon   Third Quarter

Plan Your Investigation

HANDS-ON LAB

и**Demonstrate** Go online for a downloadable worksheet of this lab.

1. You will model each view of the moon that is shown in the diagram. Look at the images of the moon. What do you think causes the differing amounts of lit moon in each image? Remember that the moon reflects light from the sun. Then think about the materials in the list. What do you think each material could represent in your model?

2. Start by discussing how you could model the view called *First Quarter*. Decide where you could position the flashlight and foam balls to show the sun, Earth, and moon in orbit. Where will you position the moon so an observer on Earth would see the first quarter moon? (Hint: Observe that during the first quarter phase, the right side of the moon is lit and the left side is dark.)

3. The next phase after first quarter is full moon. Based on this information, decide how to model the moon's orbit around Earth. In other words, in which direction does the moon orbit Earth?

4. Decide how to model the full moon, the third quarter, and the new moon. Where in its orbit does the moon take on each shape as seen from Earth?

5. Record your plans for modeling the phases of the moon. Include sketches or drawings that will help you to construct your model. Review your plans with your teacher before building and testing your model.

Plan

_____

_____

_____

_____

_____

_____

_____

_____

_____

_____

_____

_____

_____

_____

Sketches

Analyze and Interpret Data

1. **SEP Develop Models** In your model, where did you place the flashlight, large foam ball, and small foam ball to model the first quarter moon?

....

....

....

....

....

2. **CCC Patterns** Compare and contrast your models of the first quarter moon and the third quarter moon. What causes these shapes to look different to an observer on Earth?

....

....

....

....

....

3. **SEP Apply Scientific Reasoning** At the first and third quarter phases, the moon's shape appears as half a circle. Why do you think these phases are called *quarter* phases and not *half* phases?

....

....

....

....

....

4. **SEP Construct Explanations** One lunar cycle includes all of the lunar phases. One lunar cycle is about one month long. Use evidence from your model to describe how the motions of the moon lead to lunar phases that occur in a lunar cycle.

....

....

....

....

Solar System and the Universe

How do astronomers
use telescopes and
space probes to study
the universe?

☑**Connect** Develop a model to compare Earth's size to the size of the other planets.

What questions do you have about the phenomenon?

....

....

....

....

....

....

....

....

....

HANDS-ON LAB

ʋInvestigate Develop a model to describe the role of gravity in the solar system.

MS-ESS1-2 Develop and use a model to describe the role of gravity in the motions within galaxies and the solar system.

MS-ESS1-3 Analyze and interpret data to determine scale properties of objects in the solar system.

Connect It !

✎ **Put an X on the object in the center of the solar system. Draw a circle around Earth.**

SEP Use Models List all the objects you can identify.

....

....

CCC System Models What do the curved lines in the illustration represent? How can you tell?

....

....

Understanding the Solar System

Our home, Earth, is a planet. Earth is just one of many objects that make up our solar system. The **solar system** consists of the sun, the planets, their moons, and a variety of smaller objects. Each object in the solar system has a unique set of **features**. The sun is at the center of the solar system, with other objects orbiting around it. The force of the sun's gravitational pull keeps objects in their orbits around it. The strength of the gravitational force between any two objects in the solar system depends on their masses and the distance between them.

HANDS-ON LAB

Model the movements of planets around the sun.

Academic Vocabulary

The term *feature* can be used to mean a trait or characteristic. What are some features of the mode of transportation you use to get to school each day?

....

....

....

....

Objects in the Solar System

Figure 1 In the solar system, planets and other objects orbit the sun.

Distances in the Solar System Distances between objects in the solar system are so large that they are not easily measured in meters or kilometers. Instead, scientists frequently use a unit called the **astronomical unit** (AU). One astronomical unit equals the average distance measured from the center of the sun to the center of Earth, which is about 150,000,000 kilometers. The entire solar system extends more than 100,000 AU from the sun.

Math Toolbox

Converting Units of Distance

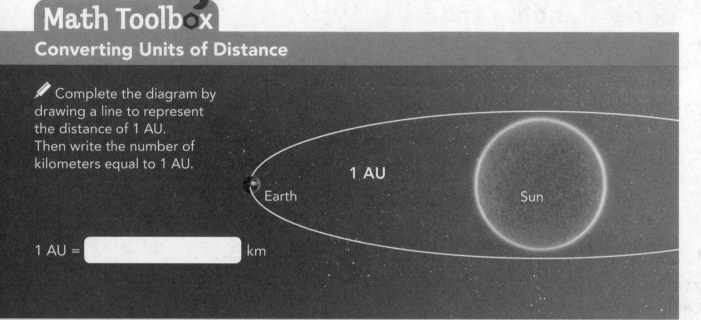

✎ Complete the diagram by drawing a line to represent the distance of 1 AU. Then write the number of kilometers equal to 1 AU.

1 AU

Earth

Sun

1 AU = [   ] km

The distances between objects in the solar system are vast. As a result, scientists use the larger value of the astronomical unit to make the numbers easier to work with.

To give you some perspective, the combined length of about 18 football fields is equal to 1 mile. One mile is about 1.6 km. That means 1 AU is equal to 1,650,000,000,000 football fields!

1. **Convert Measurement Units** Jupiter, the largest planet in our solar system, is about 630,000,000 km from Earth. About how many AU is Jupiter from Earth? Show your conversion equation, including a variable to represent the unknown answer.

....

2. **CCC Scale, Proportion, and Quantity** Develop your own conversion between AU and a common distance such as the length of a football field. How many of your common units is equal to 1 AU?

....
....
....
....

Comparing the Sun and Planets Our solar system has the sun at its center. The **sun** is a gaseous body much larger than anything else in the solar system. In fact, the sun accounts for about 99.85 percent of the entire mass of the solar system. Despite being more than a million times the volume of Earth, our sun is actually a very ordinary mid-sized star. Astronomers have used telescopes to observe stars that are a thousand times more massive than the sun. Our ordinary star is expected to continue burning for another five billion years.

A **planet** is round, orbits the sun, and has cleared the area of its orbit of any debris. The four inner planets, including Earth, are closer to the sun, small, and made mostly of rock and metal. The four outer planets are farther from the sun, very large, and made mostly of gas and liquid. Like Earth, each planet has a "day" and a "year." A planet's day is the time it takes to rotate on its axis. A planet's year is the time it takes to orbit the sun.

☑ CHECK POINT **Summarize Text** How do the inner and outer planets differ in size?

....

....

....

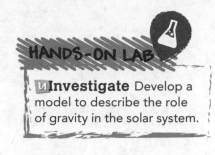

HANDS-ON LAB

✏**Investigate** Develop a model to describe the role of gravity in the solar system.

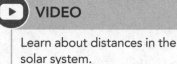

▶ VIDEO

Learn about distances in the solar system.

Comparing the Sun and Earth
Figure 2 ✏ Circle the word that correctly completes each statement in the table.

Earth	Sun
Earth is a (star/planet).	The sun is a (star/planet).
Earth is (larger/smaller) than the sun.	The sun is (larger/smaller) than Earth.
Earth is made mostly of (gas/rock).	The sun is made mostly of (gas/rock).

Note: Sun and Earth are not to scale.

Mercury
Mass: 0.330×10^{24} kg
Equatorial Diameter: 4,879 km
Distance from the sun: 0.39 AU
Orbital period: 88.0 Earth days
Moons: 0
Mean Temperature: 167°C
Atmospheric Composition: None (thin exosphere made up of atoms blasted off surface by solar wind)

During the day, temperatures on Mercury can reach 430°C. But without a real atmosphere, temperatures at night plunge to –170°C.

Earth
Mass: 5.97×10^{24} kg
Equatorial Diameter: 12,756 km
Distance from the sun: 1 AU
Orbital period: 365.26 Earth days
Moons: 1
Mean Temperature: 15°C
Atmospheric Composition: nitrogen, oxygen, trace amounts of other gases

Our planet is the only object in the solar system known to harbor life, mainly due to the fact that liquid water exists on its surface.

Venus
Mass: 4.87×10^{24} kg
Equatorial Diameter: 12,104 km
Distance from the sun: 0.72 AU
Orbital period: 224.7 Earth days
Moons: 0
Mean Temperature: 464°C
Atmospheric Composition: carbon dioxide (with sulfuric acid clouds)

Most planets and moons in the solar system rotate from west to east. Venus, oddly, rotates from east to west.

Mars
Mass: 0.642×10^{24} kg
Equatorial Diameter: 6,792 km
Distance from the sun: 1.52 AU
Orbital period: 687 Earth days
Moons: 2
Mean Temperature: −63°C
Atmospheric Composition: mainly carbon dioxide, with nitrogen and argon

The red planet is home to the largest volcano in the solar system, Olympus Mons.

The Solar System
Figure 3 🖊 The planets' sizes are shown to scale, but their distances from the sun are not. Use the data provided to mark the position of each planet on the distance scale.

CCC Patterns Examine the data about each planet. What patterns do you observe?

....
....
....
....
....

Jupiter
Mass: 1,898 × 10^{24} kg
Equatorial Diameter: 142,984 km
Distance from the sun: 5.20 AU
Orbital period: 4,331 Earth days
Moons: 67
Mean Temperature: −110°C
Atmospheric Composition: mostly hydrogen with some helium

The Great Red Spot is one of the most noticeable features of Jupiter. This storm is so huge that two to three Earths could fit inside it.

Uranus
Mass: 86.8 × 10^{24} kg
Equatorial Diameter: 51,118 km
Distance from the sun: 19.20 AU
Orbital period: 30,589 Earth days
Moons: 27
Mean Temperature: −195°C
Atmospheric Composition: hydrogen, helium, and a small amount of methane

Viewed from Earth, Uranus rotates top to bottom instead of side to side. This is because the planet's axis of rotation is tilted at an angle about 90 degrees from vertical.

Saturn
Mass: 568 × 10^{24} kg
Equatorial Diameter: 120,536 km
Distance from the sun: 9.55 AU
Orbital period: 10,747 Earth days
Moons: 62
Mean Temperature: −140°C
Atmospheric Composition: mostly hydrogen with some helium

The particles that make up Saturn's majestic rings range in size from grains of dust to ice and rock that may measure several meters across.

Neptune
Mass: 102 × 10^{24} kg
Equatorial Diameter: 49,528 km
Distance from the sun: 30.05 AU
Orbital period: 59,800 Earth days
Moons: 14
Mean Temperature: −200°C
Atmospheric Composition: hydrogen, helium, and a small amount of methane

This planet just might be the windiest place in the solar system. Winds on Neptune can reach speeds of 2,000 kph.

☑ CHECK POINT **Integrate with Visuals** How does the size of the sun compare to the sizes of the planets?

Pluto and Ida

Figure 4 Pluto (right) was considered the ninth planet in our solar system for many years. Astronomers now classify it as a dwarf planet. Asteroid Ida (top), identified in 1884, is the first observed asteroid with a moon.

INTERACTIVITY

Investigate the factors that affect the interactions of astronomical bodies.

Smaller Solar System Objects A dwarf planet is an object that orbits the sun and has enough gravity to be spherical, but it has not cleared the area of its orbit of debris. There are five known dwarf planets in our solar system: Pluto, Eris, Ceres, Makemake (MAH keh MAH keh), and Haumea (how MAY uh). As scientists observe more distant objects, they may identify more dwarf planets.

Six of the eight planets in our solar system host at least one natural satellite, or **moon**. A natural satellite is a celestial body in orbit. Just as the sun's gravitational pull keeps the planets in their orbits, the force of gravity between a host planet and its moon keeps the moon in its orbit around the planet. Mercury and Venus both lack moons. Earth comes next, with just one moon. Jupiter and Saturn each have more than 60! Some dwarf planets also have satellites.

The solar system also includes many smaller objects that orbit the sun. Some, called **asteroids**, are small, mostly rocky bodies, many of which are found in an area between the orbits of Mars and Jupiter. **Figure 4** shows an asteroid named Ida. Chunks of rock or dust smaller than asteroids are called **meteoroids**. When entering Earth's atmosphere, a meteoroid's friction with the air creates heat that produces a streak of light called a meteor. Meteoroids that pass through the atmosphere and hit Earth's surface are called meteorites. **Comets** are loose balls of ice and rock that usually have very long, narrow orbits. They develop tails as they orbit the sun.

Solar System Formation

Scientists think the solar system formed at a minimum of 4.6 billion years ago from a cloud of hydrogen, helium, rock, ice, and other materials. The first step in the formation of the solar system occurred as the force of gravity began to pull together materials in the cloud. A rotating disk of gas, ice, and dust formed as the cloud material was drawn toward the central mass. As more material was pulled into the disk's center, it became more dense, pressures increased, and as a result, the center grew hot.

Eventually, the sun formed as temperature and pressures became so high that hydrogen atoms combined to form helium. This process releases large amounts of energy in the form of electromagnetic radiation, which includes sunlight.

Around the sun, bits of rock, ice, and gas began to pull together first from electrostatic charges, or electrical forces that do not flow. As the objects grew larger, gravity pulled them together. The rock and ice formed small bodies called planetesimals (plan uh TES suh muhllz). These planetesimals collided with each other and eventually created most of the objects that we see in the solar system, shown in **Figure 5** on the next page.

The inner planets that formed closer to the sun were relatively smaller in size and mass. Their weak gravity, combined with the hot environment, resulted in dry, rocky bodies that were unable to hold onto light gases such as helium and hydrogen. Farther away from the sun, ice combined with rock and metal in the cooler environment. The outer planets that formed were more massive. As a result, gravity exerted a strong pull on hydrogen and helium gases, forming the gas giants we know today.

INTERACTIVITY

Develop a script for an animation that shows the formation of the solar system.

Literacy Connection

Integrate with Visuals
Use the information in the text on the previous page to write captions for the four images.

Forming the Solar System

Figure 5 ✏️ The solar system formed from a cloud of gas and other materials. Write the numbers 1 through 4 to put the images in order and represent how the solar system formed.

☑ LESSON 1 Check

MS-ESS1-2, MS-ESS1-3

1. CCC Systems Describe the formation of the solar system.

....
....
....
....
....
....
....
....
....
....
....
....
....
....
....
....
....
....

2. CCC Structure and Function What is the relationship between a planet's distance from the sun and the length of its year? Explain.

....
....
....
....
....
....
....
....
....

3. Compare and Contrast Compare and contrast asteroids and meteoroids in terms of size.

....
....
....
....
....
....
....
....
....
....
....
....

4. SEP Apply Scientific Reasoning Explain why you think the solar system could or could not have formed without gravity.

....
....
....
....
....
....
....
....
....
....
....
....

Learning About the Universe

HANDS-ON LAB

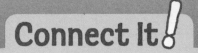**Investigate** Design and build a model of a space exploration vehicle.

MS-ESS1-3 Analyze and interpret data to determine scale properties of objects in the solar system.

Connect It!

Study the photo and answer the questions.

SEP Use Models What are some of the objects you see?

....

SEP Apply Scientific Reasoning How do you think astronomers took this image?

....

....

Collecting Space Data

With advances in engineering and technology, humans discover more about the universe every year. Astronomers define the universe as all of space and everything in it. Data from telescopes, satellites, and other instruments based both on Earth and in space are opening up the mysteries of the universe to people on Earth.

All objects in space emit, or give off, energy. This energy is known as electromagnetic radiation, or energy that can travel in the form of waves. Astronomers use instruments and tools, such as telescopes, that detect electromagnetic radiation to collect data and produce images of objects in space, such as the one in **Figure 1**.

There are many types of electromagnetic radiation, but visible light is the type that is most familiar to you. Visible light is the light you can see. If you've ever observed light shining through a prism, then you know that the light separates into different colors with different wavelengths, called a visible light spectrum. When you look at the moon or a star with the naked eye or through a telescope, you are observing visible light. There are many forms of electromagnetic radiation that we cannot see, such as radio waves.

HANDS-ON LAB

Determine how lenses affect the appearance of objects seen at a distance.

INTERACTIVITY

Explore how astronomers analyze data collected by telescopes, satellites, and probes.

Literacy Connection

Determine Central Ideas
Underline the sentence that states the central idea of the text.

A Distant Galaxy

Figure 1 This image of the distant galaxy NGC 1512 is made up of several images taken by NASA's Hubble Space Telescope. This telescope is able to detect different types of objects in space.

Optical Telescopes

Objects in space give off all types of electromagnetic radiation. **Telescopes** are instruments that collect and focus light and other forms of electromagnetic radiation. Telescopes make distant objects appear larger and brighter. Some are based on Earth and others can be found floating in space. Optical telescopes use lenses and mirrors to collect and focus visible light. There are two main types of optical telescopes. Reflecting telescopes primarily use mirrors to collect light. Refracting telescopes use multiple lenses to collect light.

Other Telescopes

Scientists also use non-optical telescopes to **complement** data obtained by other methods. These telescopes collect different types of electromagnetic radiation. Radio telescopes, such as the ones in **Figure 2**, which are operated by the California Institute of Technology, detect radio waves from objects in space. Most radio telescopes have curved, reflecting surfaces. These surfaces focus faint radio waves the way the mirror in a reflecting telescope focuses light waves. Radio telescopes need to be large to collect and focus more radio waves because radio waves have long wavelengths.

Academic Vocabulary

What does it mean when images in a book complement the text?

....

....

Radio Telescope

Figure 2 These radio telescopes are located in Owens Valley, California.

Apply Concepts Why are radio telescopes so large?

....

....

Space Probes Since humans first began exploring space, only 27 people have landed on or orbited the moon. Yet, during this period, astronomers have gathered a great deal of information about other parts of the solar system. Most of this information has been collected by space probes. A space probe is a spacecraft that carries scientific instruments to collect and transmit data, but has no human crew.

Each space probe is designed for a specific mission. Some are designed to land on a certain planet, such as the Mars rovers. Others are designed to fly by and collect data about planets and other bodies in the solar system.

Data from Probes Each space probe has a power system to produce electricity and a communication system to send and receive signals. Probes often carry scientific instruments to perform experiments. Some probes, called orbiters, are equipped to photograph and analyze the atmosphere of a planet. Other probes, called landers, are equipped to land on a planet and analyze the materials on its surface. Telescopes, satellites, astronauts, and probes have all contributed to our growing knowledge of the solar system and our universe. Space exploration is now limited only by technology, our imaginations, and the availability of funding.

☑ **CHECK POINT** **Determine Meaning** Why do you think space-craft that carry instruments to collect data about objects in space are called probes?

....

....

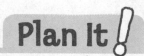
Plan It

Space Probe Mission

SEP Use Models The flowchart shows the stages of a space probe mission to Mars. Write captions to describe the stages of the space probe mission.

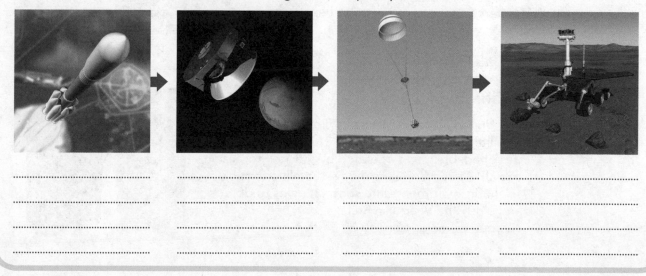

....

....

....

....

History of Space Exploration

The advent of rocket technology in the 1940s led to a new era of space exploration, detailed in the timelines in **Figure 3** and **Figure 4**. Astronomers were no longer bound to ground-based observations, as humans, telescopes, and space probes were sent into space.

1947 Fruit Flies Launched into Space

Uncertain of the effects of space-travel on organisms, NASA begins experimentation on the effects of space exposure by launching a container of fruit flies into space to see how it affects them. Their container parachutes back to Earth and the fruit flies are recovered alive and in apparent good health.

1957 Laika Goes to Space

The Soviet Union also seeks to test the effects of space-travel on living organisms. The Soviets launch a dog named Laika into space on board a small craft called *Sputnik II*. She was the first animal ever to orbit Earth. Sadly, she died in space during the mission.

1940s

1950s

1957 *Sputnik I*

The Soviet Union launches *Sputnik I*, Earth's first artificial satellite, on October 4, 1957. This tiny craft, about the size of a beach ball and weighing little more than 80 kg, orbits Earth in 98 minutes. Its launch marks the start of the space age and a fierce space-race between the United States and the Soviet Union.

1958 *Explorer I*

The United States launches its first artificial satellite into space on January 31, 1958. *Explorer I*, designed, built, and operated by the Jet Propulsion Lab (JPL) in California, is the first satellite to carry scientific instruments into space. It helps to detect and study the Van Allen Belts, strong belts of charged particles trapped by Earth's magnetic field.

1973 Skylab

Long before the International Space Station (ISS), NASA builds America's first space station, Skylab, in 1973. It orbits Earth until 1979 with the objective of helping scientists to develop science-based crewed space missions. Weighing more than 77,000 kg, Skylab I includes a workshop, a solar observatory, and systems to allow astronauts to spend up to 84 days in space.

1977 Voyager 1 & 2

One of the greatest missions to explore our solar system is led by twin space-probes called *Voyager 1* and *Voyager 2*. The two spacecraft are the first human-made objects to visit the planets of the outer solar system. Their instruments help scientists to explore and study Jupiter, Saturn, Uranus, Neptune, and many of their moons.

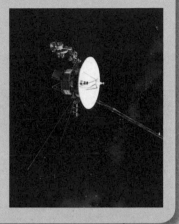

1961 First Person to Orbit Earth

On April 12, 1961, Soviet Yuri Gagarin becomes the first person to travel into space and orbit Earth. His 108-minute mission circles the Earth once and reaches a maximum altitude of about 300 kilometers.

1960s

1970s

1962 *Mariner 2* to Venus

NASA launches *Mariner 2* toward Venus on August 27, 1962. It is the first human-made object to study another planet from space. As *Mariner 2* flies by Venus, its sensors send back data on the Venusian atmosphere, magnetic field, and mass. Its instruments also take measurements of cosmic dust and solar particles before and after passing the planet.

1969 Moon Landing

Three American astronauts travel to the moon aboard *Apollo 11*. As Michael Collins pilots the command module *Columbia* above, Neil Armstrong and Buzz Aldrin land the lunar module *Eagle* on the moon and become the first humans to walk on its surface.

Space Exploration from the 1940s to the 1970s

Figure 3 🖊 Early space exploration involved some missions that carried people and some that did not. In each circle on the timeline, write *U* if the mission was uncrewed, or *C* if the mission was crewed.

📓 **Write About It** Scientists sent animals into space before they ever considered sending humans. In your science notebook, explain why you think humans were sent only after animals went into space.

1981 The Space Shuttles

First lifting off in 1981, the U.S. space shuttle is able to take off like a rocket and land like a plane, making it the first reusable spacecraft. Over the next 30 years, a fleet of five shuttles will be built and fly 135 missions carrying astronauts and cargo into space. Boasting a large cargo bay and lots of room for a crew, the shuttles make it possible for astronauts to launch and repair satellites, conduct research, and assist in the building of the ISS.

1998 The International Space Station (ISS)

Construction begins on the ISS, which requires more than 115 space flights to build. With a mass of nearly 420,000 kg, the ISS is almost five times larger than Skylab. About the size of a football field, it is the largest human-made structure ever built in space. A truly international effort, the ISS is a space-based laboratory and observatory used by scientists from around the world to conduct research that requires or focuses on the conditions found in space.

1980s

1990s

1990 Hubble Space Telescope

Carried aboard the space shuttle *Discovery* on April 24, 1990, the Hubble Space Telescope is the first space observatory located in space. Orbiting about 550 km above Earth and its blurry atmosphere, Hubble uses advanced visible-light optical technology to study the most distant objects in our solar system—stars and exoplanets in the Milky Way, as well as the farthest galaxies in the universe.

1997 Cassini-Huygens

A joint project between the United States and Europe, the Cassini mission launches on October 15, 1997, on a 3.5-billion-km journey to study Saturn, its ring system, and its many moons. Cassini also carries the Huygens Probe, which captures photos of Saturn's largest moon, Titan, while landing on its surface. The mission's many discoveries include rivers and lakes of liquid hydrocarbons on Titan's surface, making it the only known place in the solar system besides Earth where matter exists as a liquid on the surface. The spacecraft, which was operated by JPL in California, plunged into Saturn as it ended its mission on September 15, 2017.

2003 Mars Exploration Rovers

In 2003, NASA launches two rovers—*Spirit* and *Opportunity*—to land on and explore Mars. Their missions are to search for signs of past life. Using wheels to move around, instruments to drill and test rock and soil samples, and several sophisticated cameras, the rovers help scientists find evidence that Mars was once a wet, warm world capable of supporting life.

2009 Kepler

Seeking to answer the question of how unique our solar system is, NASA launches the Kepler Space Telescope in 2009, with instruments specially designed to search for planets outside our solar system. The Kepler mission focuses on studying a small part of the sky, counting the number and type of exoplanets it finds, and then using those data to calculate the possible number of exoplanets in our galaxy.

2000s   Present

2003 Spitzer Space Telescope

In August of 2003, NASA launches the Spitzer Space Telescope. Spitzer uses an 85-cm infrared telescope capable of seeing heat to peer into regions of space that visible-light telescopes such as the Hubble have difficulty seeing or seeing through. Using Spitzer, scientists can more easily study exoplanets, giant clouds of cool molecular gas and organic molecules, and the formation of new stars. Spitzer is operated and managed by the Jet Propulsion Lab and the Spitzer Science Center, located at the California Institute of Technology.

Space Exploration from the 1980s to Present

Figure 4 ✏ As space exploration evolved, missions changed in focus to studying more distant objects. Continue to write *U* for uncrewed missions and *C* for crewed missions.

CCC Patterns Describe any patterns you observe in the development of space exploration.

2012 *Voyager 1* Leaves the Solar System

On August 25, 2012, *Voyager 1* leaves the area of the sun's influence and enters interstellar space, becoming the first human-made object to leave the solar system. It continues to assist scientists by transmitting data on its location and the density of plasma it encounters at the boundaries of our solar system.

....

....

....

....

....

1. CCC Communicate Information Identify a spacecraft operated by human beings and describe how it helped add to our knowledge of space.

....

....

....

....

....

....

....

....

....

....

....

....

2. Connect to Technology Which space technology used today contributes the most to our understanding of distant stars? Explain your answer.

....

....

....

....

....

....

....

....

....

....

....

3. CCC Structure and Function  Choose two tools that astronomers use to learn more about objects in the universe. Draw a Venn diagram to compare and contrast how the tools function and the kinds of data they collect.

BLAST OFF!

INTERACTIVITY

Launch a Space Probe

How do you get a

space probe into outer space? You engineer it! Rocket technology shows us how.

The Challenge: To get a space probe on its way to Pluto and beyond.

Phenomenon In 2006, the *New Horizons* space probe was launched from Cape Canaveral, Florida. The probe was destined for the outer reaches of our solar system, studying the dwarf planet Pluto in a flyby encounter from 2015 to 2016. The Atlas V rocket was used to launch the probe on its long, 4-billion-km (2.5-billion-mile), journey. This powerful rocket, like many other rockets used to launch satellites and probes into space, is made up of two major sections called stages.

The payload carries the *New Horizons* space probe and the second-stage Centaur engine.

The Atlas V booster is the main part of the rocket that helps thrust the craft upward and releases it from Earth's gravitational pull.

The solid booster rockets provide additional thrust and then fall away not long after the launch.

DESIGN CHALLENGE

Can you design and build a model of a rocket? Go to the Engineering Design Notebook to find out!

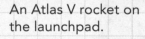

An Atlas V rocket on the launchpad.

Stars and Galaxies

HANDS-ON LAB

uInvestigate Develop a model of the Milky Way.

MS-ESS1-2 Develop and use a model to describe the role of gravity in the motions within galaxies and the solar system.

Connect It!

Study the photo and answer the questions.

Explain Based on what you see, how do you think scientists measure the distances between objects in space?

....

....

SEP Define Problems What are some challenges that you think scientists face when trying to study other regions of space?

....

....

....

How Stars Are Organized

The brightest and largest spots of light that you see in **Figure 1** are galaxies. There are estimated to be billions of galaxies, and each of these galaxies is made up of many billions of stars. Measuring the distances between Earth and these objects poses a challenge to astronomers because the distances are so vast.

Parallax When trying to **determine** the distance to nearby stars and other objects, astronomers measure the object's apparent motion in the sky as Earth is on opposite sides of its orbit around the sun. This apparent motion of the object against distant background stars is called parallax.

Parallax is best used to measure the distance to nearby stars. The parallax of objects that are extremely far away is too small to be useful in obtaining an accurate measurement.

Deep in Space

Figure 1 The universe is enormous, almost beyond imagination. This image was captured by the Hubble Space Telescope in 1995 while peering into one of the darkest regions of space as seen from Earth. Astronomers were amazed to see more than 3,000 galaxies in the tiny patch of sky captured by the orbiting observatory.

HANDS-ON LAB

Investigate Develop a model of the Milky Way.

INTERACTIVITY

Find out how Hollywood goes to space.

Academic Vocabulary

What are astronomers doing when they determine something?

....

....

Star Systems

Many stars are part of groups of two or more stars, called star systems. Star systems that have two stars are called double stars or binary stars. Groups of three or more stars are called multiple star systems.

Often one star in a binary system is much brighter and more massive than the other. Even if only one star can be seen from Earth, astronomers can often detect its dimmer partner by observing the effects of its gravity. As a dim companion star revolves around a bright star, its gravity causes the bright star to wobble. In 1995, astronomers first discovered an exoplanet—one outside our own solar system—revolving around a star. Again, they detected the planet by observing the effect the planet's gravity had on the star it orbited.

Star Clusters

Many stars belong to larger groupings called clusters. All of the stars in a particular cluster formed at about the same time. An open cluster looks loose and disorganized. These clusters may contain up to a few thousand stars. They also contain a lot of gas and dust. Globular clusters are large groupings of older stars. They are round and may have more than a million stars.

Model It

Eclipsing Binary Stars

Figure 2 A dim star may pass in front of a brighter star and block it. A system in which one dim star eclipses the light from another periodically is called an eclipsing binary. Scientists can measure the brightness of the brighter star and determine when the dim star is eclipsing it.

SEP Develop Models 🖊 Use the information in the graph to complete the missing panels in the diagram. Indicate the positions of each of the stars in the binary system.

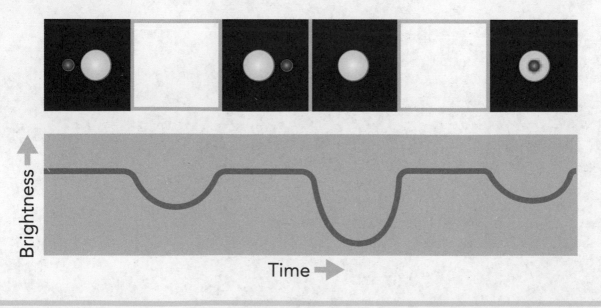

Galaxies

A **galaxy** is a group of single stars, star systems, star clusters, dust, and gas bound together by gravity. The stars in our galaxy are moving. They move around the center of the galaxy in a circular pattern. It takes millions of years for the stars to circle once around the galaxy. **Figure 3** shows several common types of galaxies.

Spiral Galaxies Spiral galaxies appear to have a bulge in the middle and arms that spiral outward like pinwheels. Our solar system is located in a spiral galaxy that we have named the Milky Way.

Elliptical Galaxies Elliptical galaxies are rounded but may be elongated and slightly flattened. They contain billions of stars but have little gas or dust between the stars. Stars are no longer forming inside them, so they contain only old stars.

Irregular Galaxies Irregular galaxies do not have regular shapes. They are smaller than spiral or elliptical galaxies. They contain young, bright stars and include a lot of gas and dust to form new ones.

Quasars Quasars are active, young galaxies with black holes at their center. Gas spins around the black hole, heats up, and glows.

Kinds of Galaxies
Figure 3 ✎ From what you know about the shapes of galaxies, label each galaxy.

👆 **INTERACTIVITY**

Explore the different types of galaxies.

117

☑ LESSON 3 Check

MS-ESS1-2

1. Identify What are the four types of galaxies?

....
....
....
....
....
....
....
....
....
....
....
....

2. CCC Cause and Effect How can astronomers detect a binary star if only one of the two stars is visible from Earth?

....
....
....
....
....
....
....
....
....
....
....
....
....
....

3. SEP Develop Models Draw and label a model that shows the role of gravity in a galaxy. Write one to two sentences explaining how gravity affects the motion of the galaxy in your model.

....
....
....
....
....
....
....
....
....
....
....
....
....
....
....
....
....
....
....
....
....
....
....
....
....
....

MS-ESS1-2

Traveling Through the
Milky Way

The Milky Way is a spiral galaxy 100,000 light-years wide. Our solar system is a small speck on one of the arms that spirals out from the center of the galaxy. Just as the planets of our solar system revolve around the sun due to gravity, the entire solar system orbits the center of the Milky Way due to the force of gravity.

Our solar system moves at 240 kilometers per second around the center of the Milky Way. At this speed, it takes 250 million Earth years for our solar system to travel all the way around!

Modern astronomy uses sophisticated tools to measure distances among objects in the Milky Way, and also to identify those objects. The Kepler space telescope, launched into Earth's orbit in 2009, has helped astronomers identify thousands of exoplanets, or planets outside our solar system. The discovery of exoplanets has helped astronomers understand that our solar system is just one of many that travels around the center of the Milky Way. Astronomers have even identified areas and exoplanets of the Milky Way that could have the right conditions to support life.

MY DISCOVERY

Search for the term *Milky Way* in an online search engine to learn more about our galaxy. What might happen to the solar system without the gravitational force exerted by the center of the galaxy?

The Milky Way is a spiral galaxy like the one shown here.

galactic center

26,100 light years

solar system

240 km/s

MS-ESS1-2

Evidence-Based Assessment

Willa is developing a model to help her study gravity. She wants to understand the role that gravity plays in keeping objects in the solar system in orbit around the sun. She plans on using some household materials to model a gravity well.

A gravity well is a representation of the gravitational field or pull of an object in space. A massive object like the sun has a deep gravity well. A less massive object, such as an asteroid, has a shallow gravity well.

Willa stretches plastic wrap across a large hoop to represent the "fabric" of space. She has one large clay ball, some small marbles, and tiny ball bearings.

When Willa places the clay ball on the plastic, she observes that it sinks into the plastic and forms a well. When she places a marble or ball bearing near the clay ball, Willa observes the marble or ball bearing roll along the surface of the plastic toward the clay ball.

1. **SEP Develop Models** In Willa's model, which of the following solar system objects does the large clay ball represent?
   A. the sun
   B. a planet
   C. a moon
   D. an asteroid

2. **CCC System Models** Willa tests her model by placing the large clay ball, a single marble, and a single ball bearing one at at time on the plastic. Which object creates the deepest well? How can these observations be applied to solar system objects? Explain.

   ....
   ....
   ....
   ....
   ....
   ....
   ....
   ....
   ....

3. **CCC Identify Limitations** Identify the limitations of Willa's model by circling the phenomena which her model cannot demonstrate.

The sun exerts a strong gravitational force on objects around it.
Planets and other solar system objects orbit the sun.
An object's gravitational force increases if the object is more massive.

4. **SEP Construct Explanations** How can Willa use the materials and her model to explain why objects that are very far from the sun do not orbit it?

   ....
   ....
   ....
   ....
   ....
   ....
   ....
   ....
   ....
   ....
   ....
   ....
   ....
   ....
   ....
   ....
   ....
   ....
   ....

Scaling Down the Solar System

How can you **build scale models** of **volcanoes** from three **planets** to show which one is largest?

Background

Phenomenon Mauna Loa in Hawaii is currently the largest active volcano on Earth. But is it the largest volcano in the solar system? Sapas Mons on Venus and Olympus Mons on Mars are two other volcanoes that can be viewed from Earth with telescopes. Scientists use scale models to help them answer questions about landforms on other planets. In this investigation, you will make scale models of volcanoes found on different planets in our solar system.

Materials

(per group)

- calculator
- graph paper
- a variety of common craft materials, such as construction paper, tape, glue, craft sticks, modeling clay, foam, cotton balls, and markers
- metric ruler

Safety

Be sure to follow all safety guidelines provided by your teacher. The Safety Appendix of your textbook provides more details about the safety icons.

Mauna Loa, Hawaii

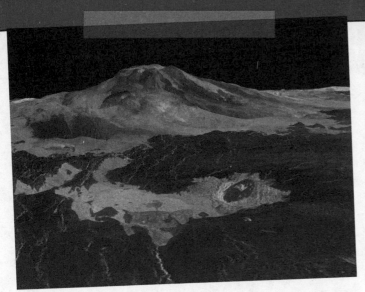

Sapas Mons

Olympus Mons

Procedure

1. Examine the images of the three volcanoes that are found on different planets in our solar system. Research the volcanoes to find out about their heights, diameters, and any other distinguishing characteristics. In the space provided on the next page, create a data table to record the names of the volcanoes, their locations, their heights (in km), and their diameters (in km).

2. Determine an appropriate scale for your models. This decision is affected by two factors: how big an area you need to model and how much detail you want to show. If you need to show a large area, then you would want to choose a smaller scale to avoid the model becoming too big. But at smaller scales, models are limited in the amount of detail they can show. Consider the details you want to show and how large or small you want the models to be. Take into account the greatest and smallest values in your data table. Choose a scale that will allow you to represent these values in the models appropriately.

   Record the scale that you will use for your models.

   1 km = _____

3. ✂ You will construct a three-dimensional model of each volcano from construction paper, modeling clay, or other available materials.

4. Draw a sketch to show your plans. Your sketch should indicate the scale of your models. It also should clearly identify the materials you will use in each part of your models. After obtaining your teacher's approval, follow your plan to construct your models to scale.

HANDS-ON LAB

и**Demonstrate** Go online for a downloadable worksheet of this lab.

Data Table

Model Sketch

Analyze and Interpret Data

1. **SEP Construct Explanations** Could you have used a different scale for each volcano to represent their relative sizes? Explain.

   ....

   ....

2. **CCC Scale, Proportion, and Quantity** Suppose someone suggested that you add a scale model of a human to your volcano models. Is this a reasonable or unreasonable suggestion? Use the scale of the models to construct your answer. (*Note: The height of a typical adult human is slightly less than 2 m, or 0.002 km.*)

   ....

   ....

   ....

   ....

3. **SEP Use Models** When you are studying models of different solar system objects, how does measuring the model objects and the distances between them, and knowing the scale of the model, help you to determine scale properties of objects in the actual solar system?

   ....

   ....

   ....

   ....

4. **Identify Limitations** Compare your models to the photographs of each volcano. What are some of the advantages of your models over the photographs? What are some of the disadvantages?

   ....

   ....

   ....

   ....

5. **SEP Evaluate Information** Using the scale models created by your class, compare characteristics such as the size and shape of the three different volcanoes found on Venus, Earth, and Mars. What can you infer about the three planets from this analysis?

   ....

   ....

   ....

MS-ESS1-3

Comparing Solar System Objects

Small solar system objects far from Earth—such as comets, dwarf planets, and asteroids—have been observed for centuries. Only in recent years have astronomers been able to make observations from up close, thanks to technological advances in telescopes and spacecraft.

Ceres

A dwarf planet in the asteroid belt between Mars and Jupiter, Ceres takes 4.6 Earth years to revolve around the sun. It is about 2.8 AU from the sun. Ceres has a core of water ice and a rocky crust made of different salts. Its crust is marked by numerous impact craters.

Vesta

An asteroid in the same asteroid belt as Ceres, Vesta is made of hardened lava. About 1 percent of Vesta was blasted into space when another object collided with it, leaving a crater 500 kilometers wide. Vesta is about 530 km wide, though it is not spherical in shape.

Titan

The largest moon around Saturn, Titan has an icy surface with rivers of liquid methane and ethane. It is 9.54 AU from the sun. With a radius of 2,575 km, it is larger than Earth's moon. Its mass is 1.3455×10^{23} kg.

Hartley 2

A comet that visits the inner solar system every 6.5 years, Hartley 2, also known as 103P, is an icy mass that spins around one axis while tumbling around another. At its closest distance, Hartley 2 is about 1.05 AU from the sun, or 0.05 AU from Earth's orbit. The outer reaches of Hartley 2's orbit takes it about 5.9 AU from the sun. The comet loses some of its icy mass each time it passes near the sun.

Complete the table that summarizes the characteristics of four small objects of the solar system. Then use the information you have gathered to answer the following questions.

	Ceres	Vesta	Titan	Hartley 2
Classification	Dwarf planet	Asteroid		
Mass (kg)	9.47×10^{20}	2.67×10^{20}		3×10^{11}
Diameter (km)	952		5,150	0.16 (nucleus)
Distance from Sun (AU)		2.5		
Composition				Ice and carbon dioxide

1. **SEP Engage in Argument** Why is Vesta considered an asteroid while its "sister" Ceres is classified by astronomers as a dwarf planet?

....

....

2. **SEP Construct Explanations** Titan's average distance from the sun is 9.54 AU, which is the same as Saturn's average distance from the Sun. Why doesn't Titan crash into Saturn?

....

....

3. **SEP Develop Models** Suppose you are given a diagram that shows the position of the planets from the sun and their relative sizes. You are asked to add the four smaller solar system objects in the chart to the model. Which of the objects' characteristics would be easier to represent in the model? Which characteristics would be difficult to represent?

....

....

....

....

Exoplanet Profile

Now that you have completed all three topics in this segment, do the following tasks.

Case Study Although thousands of exoplanets have been discovered and new ones are being identified every week, most are not considered habitable. But there are many exoplanets that astronomers are encouraged by.

The following is a list of exoplanets that astronomers have identified as being potentially habitable. Choose one of these planets to research.

- Proxima Centauri b
- Trappist-1 e
- Trappist-1 f
- Trappist-1 g
- Gliese 667 C c

- Gliese 667 C e
- Gliese 667 C f
- Kepler-442 b
- Kepler-452 b
- Kepler-1229 b

- Kapteyn b
- Kepler-62 f
- Kepler-186 f
- LHS 1140 b
- Ross 128 b

Though most exoplanets discovered so far are considered uninhabitable, astronomers think that some may be able to support life.

Communicate a Solution

Based on your research, answer the following questions.

1. SEP Analyze Data Which planet did you choose? Where is it located? How far is it from Earth?

....

....

....

....

2. CCC Scale, Proportion, and Quantity How large is your planet relative to Earth? How often does your exoplanet orbit its star?

....

....

....

....

3. CCC Patterns How far is your planet from its star compared to Earth's distance from the sun? Why do astronomers consider this within the habitable zone?

....

....

....

....

....

4. SEP Communicate Information What else is unusual or unique about your exoplanet?

....

....

....

....

....

APPENDIX A

Safety Symbols

These symbols warn of possible dangers in the laboratory and remind you to work carefully.

 Safety Goggles Wear safety goggles to protect your eyes in any activity involving chemicals, flames or heating, or glassware.

 Lab Apron Wear a laboratory apron to protect your skin and clothing from damage.

 Breakage Handle breakable materials, such as glassware, with care. Do not touch broken glassware.

 Heat-Resistant Gloves Use an oven mitt or other hand protection when handling hot materials, such as hot plates or hot glassware.

 Plastic Gloves Wear disposable plastic gloves when working with harmful chemicals and organisms. Keep your hands away from your face, and dispose of the gloves according to your teacher's instructions.

 Heating Use a clamp or tongs to pick up hot glassware. Do not touch hot objects with your bare hands.

Flames Before you work with flames, tie back loose hair and clothing. Follow your teacher's instructions about lighting and extinguishing flames.

No Flames When using flammable materials, make sure there are no flames, sparks, or other exposed heat sources present.

Corrosive Chemical Avoid getting acid or other corrosive chemicals on your skin or clothing or in your eyes. Do not inhale the vapors. Wash your hands after the activity.

Poison Do not let any poisonous chemical come into contact with your skin, and do not inhale its vapors. Wash your hands when you are finished with the activity.

 Fumes Work in a well-ventilated area when harmful vapors may be involved. Avoid inhaling vapors directly. Test an odor only when directed to do so by your teacher, and use a wafting motion to direct the vapor toward your nose.

 Sharp Object Scissors, scalpels, knives, needles, pins, and tacks can cut your skin. Always direct a sharp edge or point away from yourself and others.

 Animal Safety Treat live or preserved animals or animal parts with care to avoid harming the animals or yourself. Wash your hands when you are finished with the activity.

 Plant Safety Handle plants only as directed by your teacher. If you are allergic to certain plants, tell your teacher; do not do an activity involving those plants. Avoid touching harmful plants such as poison ivy. Wash your hands when you are finished with the activity.

 Electric Shock To avoid electric shock, never use electrical equipment around water, when the equipment is wet, or when your hands are wet. Be sure cords are untangled and cannot trip anyone. Unplug equipment not in use.

 Physical Safety When an experiment involves physical activity, avoid injuring yourself or others. Alert your teacher if there is any reason you should not participate.

 Disposal Dispose of chemicals and other laboratory materials safely. Follow the instructions from your teacher.

 Hand Washing Wash your hands thoroughly when finished with an activity. Use soap and warm water. Rinse well.

 General Safety Awareness When this symbol appears, follow the instructions provided. When you are asked to develop your own procedure in a lab, have your teacher approve your plan.

Use this space for recording notes and sketching out ideas.

A

absolute age The age of a rock given as the number of years since the rock formed.

absorption The transfer of energy from a wave to a material that it encounters.

acceleration The rate at which velocity changes.

acid rain Rain or another form of precipitation that is more acidic than normal, caused by the release of molecules of sulfur dioxide and nitrogen oxide into the air.

adaptation An inherited behavior or physical characteristic that helps an organism survive and reproduce in its environment.

amphibian A vertebrate whose body temperature is determined by the temperature of its environment, and that lives its early life in water and its adult life on land.

amplitude The height of a transverse wave from the center to a crest or trough.

analog signal A signal that allows for a continuous record of some kind of action.

artificial selection The process by which humans breed only those organisms with desired traits to produce the next generation; selective breeding.

asteroid One of the rocky objects revolving around the sun that is too small and numerous to be considered a planet.

astronomical unit A unit of distance equal to the average distance between Earth and the sun, about 150 million kilometers.

autosomal chromosomes The 22 pairs of chromosomes that are not sex chromosomes.

axis An imaginary line that passes through a planet's center and its north and south poles, about which the planet rotates.

B

bandwidth The amount of information that can be transmitted in bits per second.

birth rate The number of people born per 1,000 individuals for a certain period of time.

C

chromosome A threadlike structure within a cell's nucleus that contains DNA that is passed from one generation to the next.

clone An organism that is genetically identical to the organism from which it was produced.

comet A loose collection of ice and dust that orbits the sun, typically in a long, narrow orbit.

competition The struggle between organisms to survive as they attempt to use the same limited resources in the same place at the same time.

concave A mirror with a surface that curves inward or a lens that is thinner at the center than at the edges.

conductor A material that allows electric charges to flow.

conservation The practice of using less of a resource so that it can last longer.

constellation A pattern or grouping of stars that people imagine to represent a figure or object.

convex A mirror that curves outward or lens that is thicker in the center than at the edges.

D

death rate The number of deaths per 1,000 individuals in a certain period of time.

decibel (dB) A unit used to compare the loudness of different sounds.

deforestation The removal of forests to use the land for other reasons.

desertification The advance of desert-like conditions into areas that previously were fertile.

diffraction The bending or spreading of waves as they move around a barrier or pass through an opening.

diffuse reflection Reflection that occurs when parallel light rays hit an uneven surface and all reflect at different angles.

digital signal A signal that allows for a record of numerical values of an action at a set of continuous time intervals.

Doppler effect The change in frequency of a wave as its source moves in relation to an observer.

E

eclipse The partial or total blocking of one object in space by another.

elastic potential energy The energy associated with objects that can be compressed or stretched.

electric current The continuous flow of electrical charges through a material.

electric field The region around a charged object where the object's electric force is exerted on other charged objects.

electric force The force between charged objects.

electric motor A device that transforms electrical energy to mechanical energy.

electromagnet A magnet created by wrapping a coil of wire with a current running through it around a core of material that is easily magnetized.

electromagnetic induction The process of genrating an electric current from the motion of a conductor through a magnetic field.

electromagnetic signal Information that is sent as a pattern of electromagnetic waves, such as visible light, microwaves, and radio waves.

electromagnetism The relationship between electricity and magnetism.

electronic signal Information that is sent as a pattern in a controlled flow of current through a circuit.

ellipse An oval shape, which may be elongated or nearly circular; the shape of the planets' orbits.

embryo The young organism that develops from a zygote.

emissions Pollutants that are released into the air.

energy The ability to cause change.

equinox Either of the two days of the year on which neither hemisphere is tilted toward or away from the sun.

era One of the three long units of geologic time between the Precambrian and the present.

erosion The process by which water, ice, wind, or gravity moves weathered particles of rock and soil.

evolution Change over time; the process by which modern organisms have descended from ancient organisms.

exponential growth A rate of change that increases more and more rapidly over time.

extinct Term used to refer to a group of related organisms that has died out and has no living members.

F

fitness How well an organism can survive and reproduce in its environment.

focal point The point at which light rays parallel to the optical axis meet, after being reflected (or refracted) by a mirror (or lens).

force A push or pull exerted on an object.

fossil The preserved remains or traces of an organism that lived in the past.

fossil record All the fossils that have been discovered and what scientists have learned from them.

frequency The number of complete waves that pass a given point in a certain amount of time.

friction The force that two surfaces exert on each other when they rub against each other.

G

galaxy A huge group of single stars, star systems, star clusters, dust, and gas bound together by gravity.

galvanometer A device that uses an electromagnet to detect small amounts of current.

gene therapy The process of replacing an absent or faulty gene with a normal working gene to treat a disease or medical disorder.

generator A device that transforms mechanical energy into electrical energy.

genetic engineering The transfer of a gene from the DNA of one organism into another organism, in order to produce an organism with desired traits.

genome The complete set of genetic information that an organism carries in its DNA.

geocentric Term describing a model of the universe in which Earth is at the center of the revolving planets and stars.

geologic time scale A record of the geologic events and life forms in Earth's history.

gravitational potential energy The potential energy related to an object's vertical position.

gravity The attractive force between objects; the force that moves objects downhill.

H

heliocentric Term describing a model of the solar system in which Earth and the other planets revolve around the sun.

homologous structures Structures that are similar in different species and that have been inherited from a common ancestor.

GLOSSARY

I

inertia The tendency of an object to resist a change in motion.

information technology Computer and telecommunication hardware and software that store, transmit, receive, and manipulate information.

intensity The amount of energy per second carried through a unit area by a wave.

interference The interaction between waves that meet.

invertebrate An animal without a backbone.

K

kinetic energy Energy that an object possesses by virtue of being in motion.

L

law of conservation of energy The law that states that energy is conserved. When one object loses energy, other objects must gain it.

law of superposition The geologic principle that states that in horizontal layers of sedimentary rock, each layer is older than the layer above it and younger than the layer below it.

law of universal gravitation The scientific law that states that every object in the universe attracts every other object.

longitudinal wave A wave that moves the medium in a direction parallel to the direction in which the wave travels.

loudness The perception of the energy of a sound.

M

magnet Any material that attracts iron and materials that contain iron.

magnetic field The region around a magnet where the magnetic force is exerted.

magnetic force A force produced when magnetic poles interact.

magnetic pole The ends of a magnetic object, where the magnetic force is strongest.

magnetism The force of attraction or repulsion of magnetic materials.

mammal A vertebrate whose body temperature is regulated by its internal heat, and that has skin covered with hair or fur and glands that produce milk to feed its young.

mass extinction When many types of living things become extinct at the same time.

mechanical wave A wave that requires a medium through which to travel.

mechanism The natural process by which something takes place.

medium The material through which a wave travels.

meteor A streak of light in the sky produced by the burning of a meteoroid in Earth's atmosphere.

meteoroid A chunk of rock or dust in space, generally smaller than an asteroid.

moon A natural satellite that orbits a planet.

motion The state in which one object's distance from another is changing.

mutation Any change in the DNA of a gene or a chromosome.

N

natural resource Anything naturally occuring in the environment that humans use.

natural selection The process by which organisms that are best adapted to their environment are most likely to survive and reproduce.

net force The overall force on an object when all the individual forces acting on it are added together.

newton A unit of measure that equals the force required to accelerate 1 kilogram of mass at 1 meter per second per second.

noise Random signals from the environment that can alter the output of a signal.

nonpoint source A widely spread source of pollution that is difficult to link to a specific point of origin.

nonrenewable resource A natural resource that is not replaced in a useful time frame.

O

opaque A type of material that reflects or absorbs all of the light that strikes it.

orbit The path of an object as it revolves around another object in space.

overpopulation A condition in which the number of humans grows beyond what the available resources can support.

ozone A form of oxygen that has three oxygen atoms in each molecule instead of the usual two; toxic to organisms where it forms near Earth's surface.

---------------- **P** ----------------

penumbra The part of a shadow surrounding the darkest part.

period One of the units of geologic time into which geologists divide eras.

phase One of the different apparent shapes of the moon as seen from Earth.

pitch A description of how a sound is perceived as high or low.

pixel A small, uniform shape that is combined with other pixels to make a larger image.

planet An object that orbits a star, is large enough to have become rounded by its own gravity, and has cleared the area of its orbit.

point source A specific source of pollution that can be identified.

pollution Contamination of Earth's land, water, or air through the release of harmful substances into the environment.

potential energy Stored energy based on position or shape of an object.

protein Large organic molecule made of carbon, hydrogen, oxygen, nitrogen, and sometimes sulfur.

---------------- **R** ----------------

reference point A place or object used for comparison to determine whether an object is in motion.

reflection The bouncing back of an object or a wave when it hits a surface through which it cannot pass.

refraction The bending of waves as they enter a new medium at an angle, caused by a change in speed.

relative age The age of a rock compared to the ages of other rocks.

renewable resource A resource that is either always available or is naturally replaced in a relatively short time.

reptile A vertebrate whose temperature is determined by the temperature of its environment, that has lungs and scaly skin, and that lays eggs on land.

resonance The increase in the amplitude of a vibration that occurs when external vibrations match an object's natural frequency.

revolution The movement of an object around another object.

rotation The spinning motion of a planet on its axis.

---------------- **S** ----------------

satellite An object that orbits a planet.

scientific theory A well-tested explanation for a wide range of observations or experimental results.

sediment Small, solid pieces of material that come from rocks or the remains of organisms; earth materials deposited by erosion.

sewage The water and human wastes that are washed down sinks, toilets, and showers.

sex chromosomes The pair of chromosomes carrying genes that determine whether a person is biologically male or female.

sex-linked gene A gene carried on a sex chromosome.

slope The steepness of a graph line; the ratio of the vertical change (the rise) to the horizontal change (the run).

software Programs that encode, decode, and interpret information.

solar system The system consisting of the sun and the planets and other objects that revolve around it.

solenoid A coil of wire with a current.

solstice Either of the two days of the year on which the sun reaches its greatest distance north or south of the equator.

species A group of similar organisms that can mate with each other and produce offspring that can also mate and reproduce.

speed The distance an object travels per unit of time.

standing wave A wave that appears to stand in one place, even though it is two waves interfering as they pass through each other.

star A ball of hot gas, primarily hydrogen and helium, that undergoes nuclear fusion.

GLOSSARY

static electricity A buildup of charges on an object.

sun A large, gaseous body at the center of the solar system.

sustainable Using a resource in ways that maintain it at a certain quality for a certain period of time.

sustainable use The practice of allowing renewable resources time to recover and replenish.

T

telescope An optical instrument that forms enlarged images of distant objects.

thermal pollution A type of pollution caused by factories and power plants releasing superheated water into bodies of water.

transformer A device that increases or decreases voltage, which often consists of two separate coils of insulated wires wrapped around an iron core.

transluscent A type of material that scatters light as it passes through.

transparent A type of material that transmits light without scattering it.

transverse wave A wave that moves the medium at right angles to the direction in which the wave travels.

U

umbra The darkest part of a shadow.

unconformity A gap in the geologic record that shows where rock layers have been lost due to erosion.

V

variation Any difference between individuals of the same species.

velocity Speed in a given direction.

vertebrate An animal with a backbone.

W

wave A disturbance that transfers energy from place to place.

wave pulse A pulse of energy that travels through an electric circuit when it is closed.

wavelength The distance between two corresponding parts of a wave, such as the distance between two crests.

weight A measure of the force of gravity acting on an object.

INDEX

* Page numbers for charts, graphs, maps, and pictures are printed in italics. Page numbers for definitions are printed in boldface.

INDEX

* Page numbers for charts, graphs, maps, and pictures are printed in italics. Page numbers for definitions are printed in boldface.

INDEX

* Page numbers for charts, graphs, maps, and pictures are printed in italics. Page numbers for definitions are printed in boldface.

gravitational, *15, 25*
magnetic, 24, *25*
static electricity and, 19
Primary coils, 46
Principia (Newton), 73
Process skills. *see* **Science and Engineering Practices (SEP)**
produce, 35
Project based learning. *see* **Quest entries**
Protons, *13,* 14
Ptolemy, 64
Pull, magnetic, *24*
Push, magnetic, *24*

Q

Quasars, *117*
Quest Check-In, 10, 11, 20, 29, 36, 47, 56, 57, 67, 76, 85
Quest Findings, 11, 49, 57, 87
Quest Kickoff, 10, 56
Quest PBL, 10, 56
Question It!, 15, 44

R

Radio telescopes, *106*
Radio waves, 105
Reading and Literacy Skills
Cite Textual Evidence, 31, 71
Describe, 19
Determine Central Ideas, 105
Draw Evidence, 42
Explain, 17
Integrate with Visuals, 14, 16, 64, 102
Summarize Text, 13, 80
Verify, 28
Reflect, 19, 61, 79
Resistance, 17
Revolution, 70
Right-hand rule, *32, 39*
Rotation, 69
Rovers, *111*

S

Safety symbols, 130
Sapas Mons, *122, 123*
Satellites, 59
Saturn, 63, *99,* 100, 110, *126*

Science and Engineering Practices (SEP)
Analyzing and Interpreting Data, 4, 49, 129
Asking Questions and Defining Problems, 22, 114
Communicating Information, 7, 129
Constructing Explanations and Designing Solutions, 3, 17, 20, 29, 30, 38, 47, 49, 67, 76, 78, 85, 87, 91, 121, 125, 127
Developing and Using Models, 14, 20, 22, 27, 29, 33, 36, 47, 53, 66, 84, 87, 91, 94, 104, 107, 116, 121, 125, 127
Engaging in Argument from Evidence, 36, 53, 127
Obtaining, Evaluating, and Communicating Information, 36, 84, 125
Planning and Carrying Out Investigations, 22, 114
Using Mathematics, 46, 47
Science notebook
It's All Connected, 21
Reflect, 61, 79
Write About It, 31, 109
Scorpius, *61*
Seasonal changes, 62
Seasons, 71
Secondary coils, 46
Skills. *see* **Literacy Connection; Math Toolbox; Science and Engineering Practices (SEP)**
Sky
movement in, 62–63
night sky, *58,* 59–62
objects in, *59*
seasonal changes in, 62
tracking time in, 77
Skylab, 109
Slip rings, 45
Solar eclipses, *83*
Solar system
defined, **95**
distances in, 96
formation of, *101*
geocentric model, 64
heliocentric model, 65
objects in, *95*
smaller objects, 100, *126–127*
speed of, 119
Solar wind, 28
Solenoids, *34,* 35
Solstices, 72
Source, 44
South pole (magnetic), 24

Soviet Union, 108
Space
collecting data, 105–107
Earth's movement in, 68–75
meteors, 60
night sky, *58,* 59–62
Space exploration, *108–110*
Space probes, *107*
Space shuttles, 110
Space telescopes, *8*
Spectrum, 105
Speed, of comets, *60*
Spiral galaxies, *117, 119*
Spirit, *111*
Spitzer Science Center, 111
Spitzer Space Telescope, *5, 111*
Sputnik I, *108*
Sputnik II, *108*
Star clusters, 116
Star systems, 116
Star trails, *62*
Stars
defined, **59**
eclipses of, *116*
movement of, 62
organization of, 115–116
versus planets, 97
shooting, 60
Static discharge, 19
Static electricity, 18–19
Student discourse, 23, 44
Sun
compared to planets, *97–99*
defined, **97**
eclipse, 55
gravity and, 74, 75
interaction with moon and Earth, 86
in relation to planets, *63*
seasons and, 71

T

Telescopes, *8, 92,* **106,** *111*
Temple of Karnak, *77*
Test objects, 14
Thunder, 21
Tidal energy, 56, 57, 85
Time, 77
Titan, 110, *126–127*
Trains, 10, *11,* 35, *37*
Transformers, 46
Transit detection method, 4
Trolleys, *39*

CREDITS

Photography

Photo locators denoted as follows: Top (T), Center (C), Bottom (B), Left (L), Right (R), Background (Bkgd)

Covers

Front: Tntemerson/iStock/Getty Images; Rafe Swan/Getty Images; Stefan Christmann/Getty Images; Dudarev Mikhail/Shutterstock; Sumiko Scott/Getty Images; Back: Marinello/DigitalVision Vectors/Getty Images

Instructional Segment 2

iv: Nick Lundgren/Shutterstock; vi: RGB Ventures / SuperStock / Alamy Stock Photo; vii: Nathan B. Niyomtham/Getty Images; viii: John A. Davis/Shutterstock; ixT: Fabriziobalconi/Fotolia; Bkgd: Brian J. Skerry/National Geographic/Getty Images; x: Dale Kolke/ZUMA Press/Newscom; 000: ABN Images/Alamy Stock Photo; 008: RGB Ventures/SuperStock/Alamy Stock Photo; 010: Tingimage/Alamy Stock Photo; 012: David Toussaint/Getty Images; 017TCR: Bokeh Blur Background/Shutterstock; 017TR: Rassul Azadi/Shutterstock; 017BCR: Boonchuay1970/Shutterstock; 017BR: All Canada Photos/Alamy Stock Photo; 019: Andy Crawford/Dorling Kindersley/Science Source; 021: Dan Sullivan/Alamy Stock Photo; 023: Siiixth/Shutterstock; 025: Claire Cordier/Dorling Kindersley/Science Source; 027: Bart Sadowski/Shutterstock; 028: Beth Ruggiero-York/Shutterstock; 030: Marmaduke St. John/Alamy Stock Photo; 035TR: Simon Turner/Alamy Stock Photo; 035CR: China Images/Alamy Stock Photo; 035BR: Valentinrussanov/Getty Images; 037TR: Hero Images Inc./Alamy Stock Photo; 037B: Dave Higginson/Getty Images; 038: Pazut Wutigornsombatkul/Shutterstock; 044: Martin Shields/Alamy Stock Photo; 050: NASA; 054: Nathan B. Niyomtham/Getty Images; 056: Paul Lindsay/Alamy Stock Photo; 058: Scott Stulberg/Getty Images; 060: Halley Multicolor Camera Team, Giotto Project/ESA; 062: Dan Barr/Stocktrek Images/Getty Images; 068: Triff /NASA/Shutterstock; 072: David Clapp/Shutterstock; 073: NASA/Getty Images; 077Bkgd: EFesenko/Shutterstock; 077CR: IStock/Getty Images; 078: Lee Pettet/Getty Images; 080: Quaoar/Shutterstock; 082CL: Oorka/Shutterstock; 082BL: Chris Collins/Shutterstock; 088: Quaoar/Shutterstock; 089: Claudio Divizia/Shutterstock; 092: John A. Davis/Shutterstock; 097CL: Robert_S/Shutterstock; 097B: Ivann/Shutterstock; 098TL: JPL/NASA; 098TR: NASA/Shutterstock; 101TL: NASA; 101TR: Ivannn/Shutterstock; 104: Hubble & NASA/S. Smartt/NASA/ESA; 106: Comstock Images/Getty Images; 108TR: Sovfoto/UIG/Getty Images; 108CR: Sovfoto/UIG/Getty Images; 108BR: NASA; 109TR: NASA; 109BC: John Baran/Alamy Stock Photo; 110TR: Stocktrek Images, Inc./Alamy Stock Photo; 110CL: Everett Historical/Shutterstock; 110BL: ESA/NASA; 111TL: NASA; 111CR: Tim Jacobs/NASA; 111BL: JPL/NASA; 112: Dhoxax/Getty Images; 113: NASA; 114: Peresanz/Shutterstock; 117: NASA/S.Dupuis/Alamy Stock Photo; 119: Albert Barr/Shutterstock; 123TL: JPL/NASA; 123TR: Stocktrek Images/Getty Images.

Take Notes

Use this space for recording notes and sketching out ideas.

Take Notes

Take Notes

Take Notes

Use this space for recording notes and sketching out ideas.

Take Notes